MEDICAL RESEARCH COUNCIL

PRIVY COUNCIL

MEDICAL RESEARCH COUNCIL

SPECIAL REPORT SERIES No. 235

THE
CHEMICAL COMPOSITIO
OF FOODS

by

R. A. McCANCE AND E. M. WIDDOWSON

SECOND EDITION

LONDON : HIS MAJESTY'S STATIONERY OFFICE
1946

Price 6s 0d net

Universal Decimal Classification 613.2 : 543

PREFACE

The nutritional and dietetic treatment of disease, as well as research into problems of human nutrition, demands an exact knowledge of the chemical composition of food. The pioneering investigations into food chemistry were made in Germany and the United States of America and until after the war of 1914–18 this country lagged far behind. The research on vitamins which began to make rapid progress soon after that war, and in which this country played a leading part, stimulated a demand for a wider knowledge about human foods. Accordingly, when Dr. McCance approached the Council in 1925 for support in order that he might determine, in the first instance, the amount of carbohydrate in foods used in the treatment of diabetes, it was recognised that the project was likely to have practical importance, and a grant was made for work along these lines at King's College Hospital, London. Since that time the Council have continued to support similar and related studies by Dr. McCance and his colleagues, first at King's College Hospital and subsequently at the Department of Medicine, University of Cambridge; and during this period the investigators have gradually extended the scope of their inquiries. A system of analysis has been evolved by which they have determined all the important organic and mineral constituents of foods, with the exception of the vitamins, which have formed the subjects of extensive research by other workers and by different methods. Some idea of the amount of detailed analytical work involved in these chemical studies may be gathered from the statement that as many as twenty different constituents may require to be determined in a single foodstuff.

By 1939, when the first edition of these tables was published, this systematised analytical procedure had been applied by Dr. McCance and his colleagues to most of the foods commonly eaten in Great Britain. The method of approach had been somewhat different from that of previous workers in the same field; for the foods had been analysed, not only in the raw state, but also as prepared for the table, and studies had been made of the losses introduced by cooking. The investigators had also examined the question whether all the constituents of a food are really available for the body's use; whether they are decomposed in the alimentary canal, or fail to be absorbed. The greater part of this work was published by the Council in Reports in this Series (Nos. 135, 187 and 213). Some of the analytical data published in 1939 had already appeared in the earlier Reports, but many of them were new, and it was hoped that the first edition of these tables would contain all the quantitative data about the chemical composition of British foods likely to be required for practical work. It did not, however, in other respects supersede the three previous Reports, for the latter contained much information which was not reprinted.

The recent war and its attendant nutritional problems created a demand for analytical data, old and new, and experience and criticism led the authors to reconsider a few of the figures previously published by them, so that minor alterations and additions were made when the tables were reprinted for the third time in 1942. A new edition has now become necessary. The authors have made no change in the form of the main tables or text, but figures relating to a number of new foods and food materials have been added. These partly fill in gaps in the tables, partly replace older figures, but mostly supply information about the composition of foods which are characteristic of war-time and post-war circumstances. It was pointed out in the preface to the first edition of these tables that research of this nature is technically exacting and at the same time laborious. Almost every substance to be analysed brings up fresh problems and the solution of these problems may take weeks or even months. It is work which appeals to relatively few investigators, for the road is long and there is little prospect of making interesting discoveries by the way. Nevertheless, the steady demand for the first edition of this volume over the last six years has proved that Dr. McCance and Dr. Widdowson's contribution to knowledge has been widely appreciated, and the Council are glad to issue this new edition in the hope that it will continue to supply a want.

MEDICAL RESEARCH COUNCIL,
38, Old Queen Street,
Westminster, S.W. 1.

December, 1945.

THE CHEMICAL COMPOSITION OF FOODS

BY

R. A. McCANCE, M.D., Ph.D., F.R.C.P.,

AND

E. M. WIDDOWSON, B.Sc., Ph.D.

From the Department of Medicine, University of Cambridge

INTRODUCTION

A knowledge of the chemical composition of foods is the first essential in the dietary treatment of disease or in any quantitative study of human nutrition. Both of these have become increasingly important in recent years, and there has in consequence been a demand for better and more up-to-date information about the chemistry of food. In order to provide investigators, particularly in Great Britain, with the necessary data, analytical work has been carried out since 1925, first at King's College Hospital, London, and more recently at the Department of Medicine, Cambridge, and the present report is an attempt to set out the results in a simple and practical manner. Most of the data have already been published (McCance and Shipp, 1933 ; Widdowson and McCance, 1935 ; McCance and Widdowson, 1935 ; McCance, Widdowson and Shackleton, 1936 ; Shackleton and McCance, 1936 ; Abrahams and Widdowson, 1940), but some are now printed for the first time. Every care has been taken to render the information as true and reliable as possible. Every figure previously published has been traced to the original notebooks and scrutinised. Mistakes have inevitably been found, and these have been corrected. When there was any doubt about the validity of a figure, further samples of the food have been procured and analysed, and the most probable value given. Further, the completed tables have been compared with a number of other recent publications of a similar nature, and where the present results have shown a wide divergence from those of others, more samples have been obtained and subjected to analysis. Some notes on these discrepancies are given on pp. 8–9. Every calculation and figure has been checked by at least two persons. Nevertheless, the present report must not be taken entirely to supersede reports Nos. 135, 187 and 213, previously issued by the Council. These reports contained large sections dealing with analytical technique, the losses occasioned by cooking, and the value of hemi-celluloses and celluloses in human nutrition, which have not been reprinted. Each had an extensive bibliography, and information was also given about the scientific nomenclature of the foodstuffs. Reference should be made to these reports if such information is required. The present report is intended to be a practical handbook, and it replaces the previous ones only in so far as analytical data are concerned.

CONSTRUCTION OF THE TABLES

Arrangement, Headings and Conventions

The foods have been classified into the following groups :—cereals and cereal foods ; dairy products ; meat, poultry and game ; fish ; fruit ; nuts ; vegetables ; sugar, preserves and sweetmeats ; beverages ; beers ; condiments ; vegetable fats ; cakes and pastries ; puddings ; meat and fish dishes ; egg and cheese dishes ; sauces and soups ; vegetable dishes. The classification has been made practical rather than scientific. Thus, the cereal group includes starchy foods such as arrowroot, sago, tapioca and soya products ; the vegetable group includes tomatoes; and the fruit group, rhubarb. Bovril, Oxo, Marmite and Virol have been included among the beverages. Since any classification must necessarily be arbitrary, and difficulty may arise in locating particular foodstuffs, a full index has been given. The figures for the "cooked dishes" (pp. 98, 141) were obtained not by direct analysis but by computation. The majority of these are included in the last five of the groups mentioned above, but there are a few in the earlier groups. The preparation of these dishes, and the method used for the calculation of their composition, are described on p. 9.

Pages 25 to 111 give the composition of the foods per 100 grammes and pages 113 to 147, the composition per ounce. A conversion factor of 28·4 g./oz. has been used.

Edible material only has been analysed, and the percentage and per-ounce composition of every item except that of beer is given on this basis. The composition of the latter has been calculated per 100 c.c. and per pint. For foods that are usually served with waste, for example, fish and stone fruits, figures have also been given for the amounts of the various edible constituents that would have been obtained from 100 g. and from 1 oz. of the food as served.

In meat and fish (Report No. 187), and in mushrooms (Report No. 213), *protein nitrogen* has been differentiated from non-protein nitrogen and the former multiplied by 6·25. Bovril, Oxo and Marmite have also been dealt with in this way. In cereals, the protein has been calculated by multiplying the total nitrogen by 5·7. For jelly the factor 5·55 has been used, and for all other foods 6·25. "*Fat*" in the meat and fish is true fat as determined by von Lieberman and Szekely's (1898) method. The fat in milk and milk products, and in comb honey has been determined by methods similar to those recommended by the Association of Official Agricultural Chemists (1930). The fats in other foods have sometimes been determined by ether extraction in a Soxhlet apparatus, sometimes by von Lieberman's method, and often by both. *Available carbohydrate* is the sum of the starch and dextrins (expressed as glucose) and sugar.

In the first printing of these tables the figures 4·1, 9·3 and 4·1 were used for calculating the calorie values of protein, fat and carbohydrate respectively. These are Rubner's figures and are the ones usually employed in this country for calculating the energy values of diets (Morey, 1936). It has been pointed out, however, that since most of the figures given for carbohydrate in these tables had been expressed as glucose or invert sugar, it would have been more correct to have employed the factor 3·75 for carbohydrate (Sherman, 1937). Accordingly, this has now been done, and, for the sake of consistency and simplicity, all the carbohydrate figures have now been expressed in the same terms, *i.e.* as monosaccharides. A special note has been inserted drawing attention to this fact where cane sugar and lactose are being considered. Hence, those who use these tables for the calculation of diets, and wish themselves to convert the sum of the daily or weekly nutrients into terms of calories, should use the figure 3·75 for carbohydrate and, as before, the figures 9·3, 4·1 and 7·0 for fat, protein and alcohol respectively.

In some food tables the factors 4, 9 and 4 have been used to convert protein, fat and carbohydrate figures to calories. These factors allow for losses of calorific material in the faeces but, since it is unusual to make such an allowance for any of the other food constituents, it seems inconsistent to do so in the case of calories, and the factors 4·1, 9·3 and 3·75 (or 4·2 if the carbohydrate is expressed as starch) are therefore to be preferred.

It might perhaps be as well to point out that the calorie values of foodstuffs, determined by means of factors, are necessarily approximations. For one reason, protein, fat, carbohydrate and alcohol are not the only organic nutrients in foods. There are, for example, organic acids in many fruits, and celluloses and hemicelluloses in all plants. All of these are a source of calories to anyone eating them, but it is customary to neglect them in working out the calorie value of a diet. For another reason, as pointed out by Atwater and Bryant (see Morey, 1936), the calorie values of proteins, fats and carbohydrates from different sources are not exactly the same, and greater accuracy might be obtained, especially in the computation of unbalanced native diets, if each foodstuff were assigned characteristic factors. The average factors here employed were worked out for the calculation of mixed diets, and their use has been hallowed by convention. There does not seem to be enough evidence at present to justify abandoning them in favour of separate factors for different foodstuffs, so long as the limitations of average factors are appreciated.

Some of the figures for *sodium* (Na), *chlorine* (Cl), *calcium* (Ca) and *phosphorus* (P) are given in brackets. This has been done where salt or sodium bicarbonate was known to have been added in the preparation of the food, where the flour was known to have been enriched with calcium, or where acid calcium phosphate had been used as a raising agent. In these instances the amounts present represent the work of man and not the gift of nature. The figures, therefore, have a different significance and may be expected to vary according to different laws. All vegetables have been cooked in distilled water without added salt or alkali. The columns headed *potassium* (K), *magnesium* (Mg) and *iron* (Fe) require no comment. *Copper* (Cu) has not been determined in all the forms of meat and fish given in the tables. No figures for *sulphur* (S) were included in the two previous reports, but most of the foods which have been investigated since these were published have been analysed for sulphur (Masters and McCance, 1939). The mixed dried samples of fruits, vegetables and nuts, which had previously been used for the determination of nitrogen and phosphorus (Report No. 213), have now been analysed for sulphur. Fresh samples of onions, however, and of other vetegables which lose their volatile sulphur on being dried have had to be obtained. Since the nitrogen/sulphur ratio in meat and fish has been found to be very constant (Masters and McCance, 1939), the sulphur in most of these foods of animal origin has been calculated from the nitrogen found in the original mixed sample and an average nitrogen/sulphur ratio. For dietetic purposes this was deemed a justifiable thing to do.

The figures given for the *acid-base values* are expressed as c.c. $\frac{N}{10}$ acid or alkali and have been calculated in the usual way. Sulphur and phosphorus have been taken to be divalent. No allowance has been made for the fact that certain fruits give rise to an excretion of hippuric acid (Sherman, 1937).

The first section of the Tables, giving the composition per 100 g., contains information which is not repeated in the second section. Thus it includes a description of each food, particulars of the method of cooking and the nature of the edible material. If the analytical data are being published for the first time, particulars are also given of the number of samples pooled for analysis and of their sources. Next follows a column headed " Edible matter, as eaten, expressed as a percentage of the weight as purchased." This gives essentially the same information as the column headed F_2 in Report No. 187 and F in Report No. 213. For foods that were analysed and would have been eaten raw, it represents the percentage of edible material in the purchased food. For foods that were analysed cooked, the figure also allows for change of weight on cooking. The figure is usually less than 100, because both waste and loss of weight on cooking tend to reduce it. For a few foods however—e.g. some fish which have been fried with batter and crumbs, cooked dried pulses and stewed fruit—the figure is greater than 100, because the added batter and crumbs or the water outweigh the waste, if any, or the loss of weight on cooking.

The " 100 g." section also contains figures for water, which were found by direct determination in all the analysed foods except meat and fish, where the values were obtained " by difference." Carbohydrate has been differentiated into starch and sugar in the " 100 g." section, the starch always being expressed as glucose. For the fruits and vegetables, figures for the unavailable carbohydrate are also given. This was determined as described in Report No. 213. It was found impracticable to make this determination in cereals and other starchy foods. Figures for total nitrogen are given throughout the " 100 g." section, and figures for purine nitrogen for the meat and fish.

Throughout the tables, the minus sign (—) signifies that no estimation has been made ; *Tr.* indicates that traces of the constituent in question are known to be present. An estimation may or may not have been carried out, but in any case the amount is of no quantitative dietetic significance.

The phytic acid phosphorus in a number of foodstuffs is given on p. 148. This is expressed as a percentage of the total amount of phosphorus present. The importance of phytic acid is twofold. Firstly, its calcium and magnesium salts are very insoluble, and if the food contains much phytic acid, these insoluble salts may be precipitated in the stomach and duodenum, thus preventing the absorption and utilisation of the greater part of the calcium in the food. Secondly, the stability of phytates to intestinal disintegration prevents the phosphorus in them from being absorbed as freely as the phosphorus in other organic and inorganic compounds. (McCance and Widdowson, 1935, 1942.)

In the first edition of this book a table was given showing the ionisible (inorganic) iron in a number of foodstuffs. It was at that time thought that only such iron was likely to be available for absorption, but since then, fresh work (Oldham, 1941, Black & Powell, 1942, McCance, Edgecombe and Widdowson, 1943) has called for a complete revision of our ideas on this subject, and the table has accordingly been omitted.

Notes on Technique and some Individual Findings

The Soxhlet method of determining fat in malted foods gives results which are much too low, and certainly incorrect. It also gives much lower results than von Lieberman's (1898) method for many cereals. In all such instances the higher figures have been preferred. On the other hand, the Soxhlet method gives much higher results than von Lieberman's method for condiments containing volatile oils (see p. 97). Some representative figures for cereals and malted foods are given below.

Food.	*Fat (g/100g).* By Soxhlet method.	*Fat (g/100g).* By von Lieberman's method.	Food.	*Fat (g/100g).* By Soxhlet method.	*Fat (g/100g).* By von Lieberman's method.
All-Bran, Kellogg's	1·0	4·5	Force ..	0·9	1·9
Biscuits, digestive	13·3	20·5	Grapenuts ..	0·4	3·0
Biscuits, rusks	5·0	8·4	Malted milk (Horlick's)	1·2	8·6
Cornflakes, Kellogg's	0·1	0·8	Ryvita ..	0·5	2·1
Flour, white ..	0·5	0·9	Shredded Wheat	0·9	2·8
Flour, brown ..	0·6	2·1	Vita-Weat ..	6·0	10·3

The variation in the amounts of the elements present in different foodstuffs is enormous. The lowest concentrations are often outside the range of the analytical methods. The highest are often so remarkable that it is difficult not to comment upon them. Some of the meat and vegetable extracts are very rich in sodium chloride—even up to 25 per cent. Bovril contained more potassium than any other food analysed (3·59 per cent.). Parmesan cheese had the highest concentration of calcium (1·22 per cent.) and Marmite of phosphorus (1·89 per cent.). Carrageen moss headed the list for magnesium (0·63 per cent.) and sulphur (5·46 per cent.). Curry powder contained more than three times as much iron as any other food (75 mg. per 100 g.), while liver contained most copper (5·8 mg. per 100 g.). Of all the foods analysed, Gruyère cheese contained most nitrogen (5·9 per cent.), corresponding to 36·8 per cent. of protein.

A few notes on individual findings given in the tables and not discussed in the previous reports are set out below. All have been confirmed by the analysis of at least two and generally three mixed samples :—

1. The sodium and chlorine in packet cheese are not present in the proportions usually found in cheese.
2. Fried fish tend to contain more calcium than the same fish after being steamed. This is because it is more difficult to separate the bones in the case of the fried fish and some small bones were almost inevitably included in the analysed (edible) material.
3. The unusually high figure for sulphur in dried apricots and dried peaches is probably to be attributed to the use of sulphur dioxide as a preservative (Leach and Winton, 1920, Monier-Williams, 1927).
4. The amount of iron in glacé cherries is much higher than would be expected from the analysis of the raw fruit. It is suggested that this is due to iron contamination during stoning.
5. The relative concentrations of sodium and chlorine in cocoa powder, Bournvita and wartime chocolate indicate that alkali has been added during manufacture. Sodium chloride has evidently been added to the wartime macaroni.
6. Golden syrup contains 7 times as much sodium as chlorine. In black treacle the ratio is reversed.
7. The amount of iron found in Ovaltine (3·5 mg./100 g.) is much lower than that given by the Imperial Bureau of Animal Nutrition, 1938 (12·0 mg./100 g.).
8. The present figure for the amount of calcium in Marmite (77 mg./100 g.) is nearly thirteen times lower than that given by the Imperial Bureau of Animal Nutrition (980 mg./100 g.).

The present findings for these last two foods are believed to be approximately correct.

The Chemical Composition of Cooked Dishes containing several Ingredients, with their Recipes

By C. M. Verdon-Roe, B.A. and J. M. Parry, B.Sc.

Dietary investigations by the individual method depend upon a knowledge of the composition of cooked foods. In the last few years some extensive surveys by this method have been made, and there has been a constant demand not only for the composition of single foods, but also for the composition of cakes, puddings, etc., which are made from a mixture of ingredients cooked in some special way. Since pooled samples of all these ingredients had been analysed, it was only necessary to know the loss or gain of water introduced in the cooking process, in order to calculate an average composition for the made dish. This loss or gain of water can be determined only by actual experiment. A series of dishes has accordingly been prepared and cooked from this point of view.

Several cookery books were studied and standard recipes for the dishes were chosen. These are given below, and any food whose composition has been arrived at in this way is referred to its particular recipe. The numbering of the recipes corresponds with the numbering of the dishes in the tables. Scones and rock buns appeared to be made according to two standard recipes, one containing eggs and one not. In these cases the food has been prepared by both methods. Plain white flour was always used before the war, and hence it was necessary to use a baking powder for cakes and certain puddings. The ingredients of this baking powder were—flour, 2 parts ; tartaric acid, 2 parts ; sodium bicarbonate, 2¼ parts. One level teaspoon of baking powder was taken to weigh 3½ grammes (⅛ oz.). Salt has been added to all the savoury dishes, and one level teaspoon of salt has been taken to weigh 3½ grammes (⅛ oz.).

A study of the recipes used for the cakes will show that sometimes butter has been used, and sometimes margarine. This is because the recipe finally chosen advocated either the one or the other, and it has always been followed exactly. Apart from vitamins, the composition of any particular dish is not altered appreciably by replacing one fat by the other.

The recipes for the various dishes having been chosen, the ingredients were weighed and mixed together according to the directions. The mixture was weighed before it was cooked and again when it was ready for consumption. Any loss in weight was assumed to be due to evaporation of water. Then the composition of the cooked dish was calculated from the composition of the listed ingredients and the change in weight on cooking. In certain cases where frying was used in the preparation of the food a gain of fat complicated matters, and in these instances it was necessary to *analyse* the cooked material for fat and for water before making the calculations. For dishes that are usually eaten hot, the composition of the hot food was calculated ; for cold dishes, computations were made on the basis of the cold weight. All the foods were cooked on at least two separate occasions, and the average of the results was taken. The amount of each ingredient given is the mean of the actual amounts used for the duplicate experiments. This explains why fractions rather than whole numbers sometimes appear in the recipes.

In making cakes and other dishes it is impossible to avoid leaving some of the raw material in the mixing bowl or on the utensils. In all such cases a correction was applied to allow for this loss.

The composition of cooked dishes altered during the war, partly because of the introduction of 85 per cent. extraction flour, dried eggs and dried skimmed milk, and also because rationing led to the adoption of plainer recipes. It should be pointed out, however, that this did not necessarily lead to a less nutritious product, and the case of jam tarts may be cited as an example.

A series of " economical " dishes has been cooked, using recipes advocated by the Ministry of Food, or modified pre-war ones, with dried eggs and " Household " milk instead of the fresh materials, with less fat and sugar and with 85 per cent. flour. Dried eggs and milk have been reconstituted according to the instructions of the Ministry of Food. The baking powder consisted of : flour, 3 parts ; acid calcium phosphate, 2 parts ; sodium bicarbonate, 1 part.

Recipes

Preserves and Sweetmeats

440. Chutney, Apple

16 oz. cooking apples, peeled and cored
15 oz. onions, peeled
3½ oz. raisins
¾ pint vinegar
1 lb. sugar
½ teaspoon mustard
¼ teaspoon pepper
½ teaspoon ground ginger
2 teaspoons curry powder
1 teaspoon salt

Chop the apples and onions into small pieces. Mix all the ingredients, except the sugar, and boil gently till soft. Add the sugar and boil for a further ½ hour. Pour into jars and tie down.

441. Chutney, Tomato

2 lb. tomatoes
4½ oz. cooking apples, peeled and cored
16 oz. onions, peeled
3½ oz. sultanas
¾ pint vinegar
1 lb. sugar
½ teaspoon mustard
¼ teaspoon pepper
2 teaspoons curry powder
1 teaspoon salt

Peel the tomatoes and proceed as for apple chutney.

418. Lemon Curd

8 oz. sugar
2½ oz. butter
3 eggs
Juice of 3 lemons (4¼ oz.)

Place the butter, sugar and lemon juice in a double pan and stir till melted. Add the eggs one by one and cook slowly, stirring all the time until the mixture coats the back of a wooden spoon.

454. Toffee

8 oz. sugar
1 oz. butter
1 teaspoon vinegar
5 oz. golden syrup
1 tablespoon water

Place all the ingredients in a saucepan and heat gently till melted. Boil rapidly for 10 minutes or until a small portion, dropped into cold water, becomes brittle. Pour into buttered tins and mark into squares while still warm.

Beverages

464. Lemonade

Juice of one lemon (1¼ oz.)
1½ oz. sugar
½ pint water

Dissolve the sugar in a little hot water. Allow to cool and add to the lemon juice and remainder of the water.

Cakes and Pastries

489. Cherry Cake

8 oz. flour
8 oz. butter
8 oz. sugar
3 eggs
6 oz. glacé cherries
1 teaspoon baking powder

Beat the butter and sugar to a cream. Add each egg separately and beat well. Stir in the flour and baking powder and add the cherries cut into pieces. Bake in a moderate oven for 1½–2 hours.

490. Chocolate Cakes

4 oz. flour
3 oz. margarine
4 oz. sugar
2 eggs
¼ oz. cocoa
1 teaspoon baking powder

Cream the fat and sugar and add the well beaten eggs. Sift in the flour, cocoa and baking powder. Beat well. Half fill small cake tins and bake in a moderate oven for 20–30 minutes.

491. Coconut Cakes

8 oz. flour
3 oz. margarine
2½ oz. sugar
1 egg
2½ oz. milk
1½ oz. desiccated coconut
1 teaspoon baking powder

Mix the flour, baking powder and sugar and rub in the fat. Add the coconut. Mix to a stiff consistency with the egg and milk. Half fill small cake tins and bake in a hot oven for 15–30 minutes.

493. Currant Cake

8 oz. flour
4 oz. margarine
4 oz. sugar
2 eggs
4 oz. currants
1 teaspoon baking powder

Cream the sugar and margarine and beat in the eggs. Add the flour and baking powder and then the fruit. Bake in a moderate oven for 1½–2 hours.

497. ECCLES CAKES

8 oz. flour, 6 oz. margarine, 3¾ oz. water — Flaky pastry
2½ oz. currants
1 oz. sugar

Make the pastry, roll out, and cut into 3-inch squares. Place some currants in the middle of each square and sprinkle over half a teaspoonful of sugar. Fold in the edges, turn over and roll out. Bake in a hot oven for about 20 minutes.

498. GINGER BISCUITS

8 oz. flour
3 oz. margarine
3 oz. sugar
1 egg
3½ oz. golden syrup
¼ oz. ground ginger
1 teaspoon sodium bicarbonate

Mix the dry ingredients. Add the previously melted fat and syrup and finally the beaten egg. Form into small balls. Bake in a moderate oven for 15–30 minutes.

499. GINGERBREAD

6 oz. flour
2 oz. butter
2 oz. sugar
4 oz. golden syrup
1 egg
1¾ oz. milk
¼ oz. ground ginger
1 teaspoon sodium bicarbonate

Put the butter, sugar and syrup into a saucepan and heat gently till melted. Beat the egg well. Mix all the ingredients together and bake in a moderate oven for about 1½ hours.

501 and 502. JAM TARTS

6 oz. raw pastry (flaky or short)
6 oz. jam

or

503. JAM TARTS (economical)

5 oz. raw short pastry (economical)
2 oz. jam

Make the pastry in the usual way, roll out and cut into rounds to fit the tart tins. Fill each tart with jam and bake in a hot oven for about 15 minutes.

504. LEMON CURD TARTS

7 oz. raw short pastry
4½ oz. lemon curd (Recipe No. 448)

Make the tarts in the same way as the jam tarts.

505. MINCE PIES

10 oz. raw short pastry
5 oz. mincemeat

Roll out the pastry and cut into rounds. Place half the rounds in tart tins. Fill up with mincemeat and cover with the remaining rounds. Bake in a moderate oven for about 20 minutes.

506. OATMEAL BISCUITS

5 oz. flour
4 oz. butter
2 oz. sugar
7 oz. oatmeal
1 egg
1¼ oz. water
1 teaspoon sodium bicarbonate

Rub the fat into the flour and sodium bicarbonate. Add the oatmeal and sugar. Mix the egg with a little water and add to the flour to make a stiff dough. Roll out thinly and cut into squares. Bake in a moderate oven for 15–20 minutes.

507. OATMEAL BISCUITS (economical)

6 oz. flour
2 oz. cooking fat
1 oz. sugar
6 oz. oatmeal
1½ oz. reconstituted "Household" milk
¼ teaspoon salt

Rub the cooking fat into the flour. Add the salt, sugar and oatmeal. Mix to a stiff dough with the reconstituted milk. Roll out thinly and cut into squares. Bake in a moderate oven for 20 minutes.

508. Orange Cake

5 oz. flour
4 oz. margarine
4 oz. sugar
2 eggs
1 oz. orange juice
1 teaspoon baking powder

Cream the fat and sugar. Add the eggs slowly, beating well. Sift in the flour and baking powder, and finally mix in the orange juice. Bake in a moderate oven for 1–1½ hours.

509 and 510. Pastry, Flaky

8 oz. flour
6 oz. margarine
3¾ oz. water

Make the pastry according to the standard method described in all cookery books.

511 and 512. Pastry, Short

8 oz. flour
4 oz. margarine
3½ oz. water

Make the pastry according to the standard method described in all cookery books,

513 and 514. Pastry, Short (economical)

8 oz. flour
3 oz. cooking fat
1½ oz. water
1 teaspoon baking powder
¼ teaspoon salt

Mix together the flour, salt and baking powder. Rub in the cooking fat and mix to a stiff dough with water. Roll out and bake in a hot oven for 10–15 minutes.

515 and 516. Pastry, Potato

8 oz. flour
4 oz. cooked potato
2 oz. cooking fat
½ oz. water
1 teaspoon salt

Cream the cooking fat and potato. Add the flour and salt and mix to a stiff dough with the water. Roll out and bake in a moderate oven for 15 minutes.

517. Plain Biscuits (economical)

6 oz. flour
2 oz. margarine
2 oz. sugar
½ oz. dried egg powder
1 oz. water
1 teaspoon baking powder

Rub the margarine into the flour. Add the sugar and baking powder. Mix to a stiff dough with the dried egg powder and water. Roll out and cut into shapes. Bake in a moderate oven for 20 minutes.

518. Plain Cake (economical)

4 oz. flour
2 oz. sugar
2 oz. margarine
½ oz. dried egg powder
1½ oz. reconstituted "Household" milk
1 oz. water (for reconstituting egg)
1 teaspoon baking powder

Cream the margarine and sugar. Beat in the reconstituted egg. Add the flour and baking powder and mix to a soft consistency with the reconstituted milk. Bake in a moderate oven for 30 minutes.

519. Queen Cakes

6 oz. flour
4 oz. butter
4 oz. sugar
2 eggs
1 oz. sultanas
1 oz. currants
1 teaspoon baking powder

Cream the butter and sugar. Add the eggs one at a time and beat well. Stir in the flour and baking powder and add the fruit. Half fill small cake tins and bake in a moderate oven for 20 minutes.

520. Rock Buns

8 oz. flour
3 oz. margarine
3 oz. sugar
2 oz. currants
4 oz. milk
1 teaspoon baking powder

Rub the fat into the flour. Add the dry ingredients. Mix to a stiff dough with the milk. Place in heaps on a greased tin. Bake in a hot oven for 15–20 minutes.

521. Rock Cakes

8 oz. flour
3 oz. margarine
3 oz. sugar
1 egg
4 oz. currants
1¼ oz. milk
1 teaspoon baking powder

Rub the fat, flour, baking powder and sugar well together. Mix in the beaten egg and milk. Add the currants. Drop the mixture in small portions on to a baking sheet. Bake in a hot oven for about 15 minutes.

522. Rock Cakes (economical)

8 oz. flour
2 oz. margarine
2 oz. sugar
3 oz. sultanas
½ oz. dried egg powder
2 oz. reconstituted "Household" milk
1 oz. water (for reconstituting egg)
1 teaspoon baking powder

Rub the margarine into the flour. Mix in the sugar, baking powder and sultanas. Mix to a stiff consistency with the reconstituted egg and milk. Drop the mixture in small portions on to a baking sheet. Bake in a hot oven for 20–30 minutes.

523. Scones (with Egg)

8 oz. flour
1 oz. butter
1 oz. sugar
1 egg
4 oz. milk
1 teaspoon baking powder

Rub the butter into the flour and baking powder. Add the sugar, egg and enough milk to make a soft dough. Roll out ½ inch thick and cut into rounds. Bake in a hot oven for 10–15 minutes.

524. Scones (without Egg)

8 oz. flour
1½ oz. butter
¼ oz. sugar
5 oz. milk
1 teaspoon baking powder

Rub the fat into the flour, baking powder and sugar. Mix in the milk. Roll out and cut into rounds. Bake in a hot oven for 15–30 minutes.

525. Shortbread

8 oz. flour
4 oz. butter
2 oz. castor sugar

Beat the butter and sugar to a cream. Mix in the flour and knead till smooth. Press into a flat tin to about ½ inch in thickness. Bake in a moderate oven for 45–60 minutes.

526. Sponge Cake

2 oz. flour
2 oz. sugar
2 eggs

Whisk the sugar and eggs together in a basin over hot water till stiff. Fold in the flour Bake in a moderate oven for 20–30 minutes.

528. Welsh Cheese Cakes

6 oz. flour, 3 oz. margarine, 2½ oz. water } Short pastry
8 oz. jam
3 oz. flour
2 oz. butter
2 oz. sugar
1 egg
1 teaspoon baking powder

Make the pastry in the usual way. Line some tins with pastry and put a little jam in the bottom of each. Cream the butter and sugar, and add the egg, beating well. Sift in the flour and baking powder and mix. Spread the mixture on top of the jam. Bake in a moderate oven for about half an hour.

Puddings

529. Apple Charlotte

13½ oz. apples, peeled and cored
3 oz. fresh breadcrumbs
3 oz. suet
2½ oz. sugar
1 oz. jam
½ oz. margarine

Grease a pie dish and line with breadcrumbs. Fill the dish with alternate layers of apple, suet, sugar, jam and breadcrumbs. Cover the top with crumbs and place dabs of margarine on the surface. Bake in a moderate oven till golden brown.

530. Apple Dumpling

6 oz. flour, 3 oz. butter, 2½ oz. water } Short pastry	3 apples (18½ oz. peeled and cored)
	1½ oz. sugar

Make the pastry. Divide into three and roll out. Peel and core the apples. Place one on each piece of pastry. Fill the centre of the apple with sugar. Work the pastry round the apple until it is well covered. Bake for 30–40 minutes in a moderate oven.

531. Apple Pudding

8 oz. flour, 4 oz. suet, 4½ oz. water, 1 teaspoon baking powder } Suet crust	10 oz. apples, peeled and cored
	3 oz. sugar
	1 oz. water

Make the suet crust. Roll out and line a basin. Trim off the uneven edges. Fill with peeled apples and a little water and sugar. Roll out the trimmings to cover the basin. Steam for 1½–2 hours.

532. Apple Tart

6 oz. raw short pastry	2 oz. sugar
8 oz. apples, peeled and cored	1 oz. water

Place the prepared apples, sugar and water in a pie dish. Roll out the pastry and place over the dish. Bake in a moderate oven for 30–40 minutes.

533. Banana Custard

1 pint milk, 1 oz. custard powder, 1½ oz. sugar } Custard	6 bananas

Make the custard (Recipe No. 545) and slice the bananas into it. Serve when cold.

534. Blancmange

1 pint milk	1½ oz. sugar
1½ oz. cornflour	

Mix the cornflour to a smooth paste with a little of the milk. Heat the remainder of the milk and sugar together. When hot stir into the paste and then transfer the whole to the saucepan. Cook gently with stirring for about 5 minutes. Turn into a mould and allow to set.

535. Bread Pudding (economical)

8 oz. stale bread	8 oz. water for reconstituting egg and for soaking bread
2 oz. flour	1 teaspoon ground ginger
1 oz. sugar	½ teaspoon baking powder
2 oz. cooking fat	¼ teaspoon sodium bicarbonate
3 oz. sultanas	
1 oz. dried egg powder	
1 oz. reconstituted "Household" milk	

Soak the bread in water for 5–10 minutes. Drain and break up with a fork. Mix in the flour, sugar, sultanas, ginger and baking powder. Mix to a soft consistency with melted cooking fat and reconstituted egg. Dissolve the bicarbonate in the reconstituted milk and add last. Bake in a moderate oven for about 45 minutes.

536. Bread and Butter Pudding

1 pint milk	1 oz. currants
1 oz. sugar	2½ oz. bread
2 eggs	¾ oz. butter

Cut the bread very thinly and spread with butter. Beat the eggs with the sugar and add the milk. Place the bread and the currants in a pie dish in alternate layers. Pour the egg and the milk over the bread and bake in a moderate oven for about 30 minutes.

537. Cabinet Pudding

¾ pint milk	2 oz. raisins
1½ oz. sugar	3 oz. bread
2 eggs	½ oz. butter

Spread the bread with butter and cut into dice. Mix the egg, sugar and milk and pour over the bread and raisins. Soak for about half an hour. Pour into a greased basin, cover with greased paper and steam slowly till set.

538. Canary Pudding

6 oz. flour
4 oz. butter
4 oz. sugar
2 eggs
½ oz. milk
1 teaspoon baking powder

Cream the butter and sugar together and beat in the eggs. Stir in the flour, baking powder and milk. Bake in a moderate oven for 30–45 minutes.

539 and 540. Castle Pudding (Baked or Steamed)

3 oz. flour
2 oz. butter
1 egg
2 oz. sugar
½ teaspoon baking powder

Cream the butter and sugar together and beat in the egg. Add the flour and baking powder. Put in greased dariole tins and bake in a moderate oven for about 20 minutes or steam for one hour.

541. Chocolate Mould

1 pint milk
2 oz. sugar
1¾ oz. cornflour
¼ oz. cocoa

Mix the cornflour and cocoa to a smooth paste with a little of the milk. Heat the rest of the milk and the sugar. Pour the hot liquid on to the paste. Return to the pan and boil for 5 minutes, stirring all the time. Pour into a mould and allow to set.

542. College Pudding

2 oz. breadcrumbs
2 oz. suet
2 oz. sugar
1 oz. currants
1 oz. sultanas
1 egg
1 teaspoon baking powder

Mix all the dry ingredients together. Add the egg, previously well beaten, and stir till thoroughly mixed. Put the mixture into greased dariole tins and bake for 25 minutes.

543. Custard, Egg (Baked

1 pint milk
2 eggs
1 oz. sugar

Beat the eggs and sugar together. Add the milk and place in a greased pie dish. Stand in a pan of water and bake in a moderate oven until set. (About 40 minutes.)

544. Custard, Egg (Boiled)

1 pint milk
2 eggs
2 oz. sugar

Beat the eggs and sugar together. Boil the milk and pour over the mixture, stirring all the time. Return to the pan. Stir for a few minutes until the mixture thickens and coats the back of a spoon. Remove from the fire immediately. Allow to cool.

545. Custard, Powder

1 pint milk
1 oz. custard powder
1½ oz. sugar

Blend the custard powder with a little of the milk. Add the sugar to the remainder of the milk, bring to the boil and pour immediately over the paste, stirring all the time. Allow to cool.

546. Custard Tart

8 oz. flour
4 oz. margarine } Short pastry
3½ oz. water
½ pint milk
1 egg
1 oz. sugar

Make the pastry and line a shallow tin. Make the custard (Recipe No. 543) and use as filling. Bake in a moderate oven till set.

547. Dumpling

4 oz. flour
1½ oz. suet
3½ oz. water
1 teaspoon baking powder

Mix all the ingredients together with cold water to form a soft dough. Divide into twelve balls. Flour each one and place in boiling water. Boil for half an hour.

548. Gooseberry Tart

6 oz. raw short pastry	2 oz. sugar
8 oz. gooseberries	1 oz. water

Place the prepared gooseberries, sugar and water in a pie dish. Roll out the pastry and place over the dish. Bake in a moderate oven for 30–40 minutes.

549. Gooseberry Tart with Potato Pastry (economical)

10 oz. raw potato pastry	2 oz. water
12 oz. gooseberries	Saccharin to sweeten

Place the gooseberries, saccharin and water in a pie dish. Make the pastry, roll out and place over the dish. Bake in a moderate oven for 45–60 minutes.

550. Jam Omelette

2 eggs	1 oz. jam
¼ oz. butter	½ oz. sugar

Beat the yolks and sugar together. Whisk the whites stiffly and fold into the yolks. Pour the mixture into an omelette pan and cook until well risen. Brown slightly under the grill. Spread with jam and fold into two.

551. Jam Roll, Baked

8 oz. flour } Short pastry	6 oz. jam
4 oz. margarine } Short pastry	
3½ oz. water } Short pastry	

Make the pastry. Roll out and spread with jam. Damp the edges and roll up. Bake in a moderate oven for 40–50 minutes.

552. Jelly

6½ oz. jelly cubes	Water

Dissolve the jelly cubes in hot water. Make up to a pint with water. Pour into a mould and allow to set.

553. Jelly (Milk)

6½ oz. jelly cubes	Water
½ pint milk	

Dissolve the jelly cubes in as little hot water as possible. Allow to cool. Add half a pint of milk slowly, stirring all the time. Make up to a pint of mixture with water. Leave to set in a mould.

554. Pancakes

4 oz. flour	2 oz. sugar
½ pint milk	1½ oz. margarine
1 egg	

Break the egg into the flour, add a little milk and stir till smooth. Add the rest of the milk by degrees, beating all the time. Allow to stand for an hour. Heat a little margarine in a frying pan. Pour into the pan enough batter just to cover the bottom thinly. Cook both sides and then turn on to sugared paper. Repeat till all the batter is used up. (Sufficient for about 12 small pancakes.)

555. Plum Tart

6 oz. raw short pastry	2 oz. sugar
8 oz. plums (weighed with stones)	1 oz. water

Place the plums, sugar and water in a pie dish. Roll out the pastry and cover the dish. Bake in a moderate oven for about 30–40 minutes.

556. Queen of Puddings

½ pint milk	1 oz. butter
2 oz. breadcrumbs	1 oz. sugar
2 eggs	2 oz. jam

Pour the heated milk and butter over the breadcrumbs and sugar. Allow to stand for a few minutes. Add the beaten yolks and pour into a greased pie dish. Bake in a moderate oven till set (20 minutes). Remove from the oven and spread with jam. Whisk the whites stiffly and pile on top. Return to a slow oven and bake till golden brown.

557. Rhubarb Tart

6 oz. raw short pastry
8 oz. rhubarb
2 oz. sugar
1 oz. water

Place the prepared rhubarb, sugar and water in a pie dish. Roll out the pastry and cover the dish. Bake in a moderate oven for about 30–40 minutes.

558. Rice Pudding

1 pint milk
2 oz. rice
1 oz. sugar
1 oz. butter

Place the rice, milk, butter and sugar in a pie dish. Bake in a slow oven for about 2 hours.

559. Rice Pudding (economical)

2 oz. "Household" milk powder
1 pint water
2 oz. rice
½ oz. sugar
½ oz. margarine

Place the rice, sugar, margarine and reconstituted milk in a pie dish. Bake in a slow oven for 3 hours, stirring occasionally during cooking.

560. Sago Pudding

1 pint milk
2 oz. sago
1½ oz. sugar

Soak the sago in the milk for 20 minutes. Add the sugar and bake in a slow oven for 30 minutes.

561. Semolina Pudding

1 pint milk
2 oz. semolina
1½ oz. sugar

Heat the milk and sprinkle in the semolina. Bring slowly to the boil and simmer till the grain is soft. Add the sugar and pour into a pie dish. Bake in a moderate oven for about 20 minutes.

562. Suet Pudding, Plain

2 oz. flour
2 oz. breadcrumbs
2 oz. suet
1½ oz. sugar
3½ oz. milk
1 teaspoon baking powder

Place all the dry ingredients together in a basin. Mix to a soft paste with the milk. Pour into a greased basin. Steam for 2½ hours.

563. Suet Pudding with Raisins

2 oz. flour
2 oz. breadcrumbs
2 oz. suet
2 oz. raisins
1½ oz. sugar
3½ oz. milk
1 teaspoon baking powder

Place the flour, breadcrumbs, suet, sugar and baking powder in a basin and mix to a soft paste with the milk. Add the raisins and mix well. Pour into a greased basin. Steam for 2½ hours.

564. Suet Pudding with Sultanas (economical)

6 oz. flour
2 oz. suet
2 oz. sugar
3 oz. sultanas
5 oz. reconstituted "Household" milk
1 teaspoon baking powder

Mix together flour, suet, sugar and baking powder. Make to a soft dropping consistency with reconstituted milk. Pour into a greased basin and steam for 3 hours.

565. Syrup Sponge Pudding (economical)

4 oz. flour
2 oz. sugar
2 oz. margarine
2¾ oz. golden syrup
½ oz. dried egg powder
1 oz. reconstituted "Household" milk
1 oz. water for reconstituting egg
½ teaspoon baking powder

Cream the margarine and sugar together and add the beaten reconstituted egg. Add the flour and baking powder and mix to a stiff dropping consistency with milk. Cover the sides and bottom of a basin with the syrup, put in the mixture and steam for 3 hours.

566. Tapioca Pudding

1 pint milk
2 oz. tapioca
1½ oz. sugar

Pour the milk over the tapioca and allow to stand for half an hour. Add the sugar. Bake in a slow oven for 20 minutes.

567. Treacle Tart

12 oz. raw short pastry
10 oz. golden syrup
1¾ oz. fresh breadcrumbs

Line shallow tins with pastry. Pour in the golden syrup. Sprinkle with breadcrumbs. Bake in a hot oven for about 30 minutes.

568. Trifle

3¼ oz. sponge cake
2¾ oz. jam
1 pint powder custard (Recipe No. 545).

Pour the custard over the sponge cakes, which have been previously cut into slices and spread with jam. Allow to cool.

569. Yorkshire Pudding

½ pint milk
4 oz. flour
1 egg
¾ oz. dripping
1 level teaspoon salt

Salt the flour and break the egg into it. Beat till smooth, gradually adding about half the milk. Add the remainder of the milk and allow to stand for at least half an hour. Pour into a tin containing very hot dripping. Bake in a hot oven for 30 minutes.

570. Yorkshire Pudding (economical)

4 oz. flour
1 oz. cooking fat
½ oz. dried egg powder
11 oz. water
1 teaspoon baking powder
1 teaspoon salt

Mix together the flour, salt, baking powder and dried egg powder. Add the water and beat well. Allow to stand for 1 hour. Pour into a tin containing the hot cooking fat. Bake in a hot oven for 30 minutes.

Meat and Fish Dishes

571. Beef Steak Pudding

Suet crust:
6 oz. flour
2 oz. suet
4 oz. water
1 teaspoon baking powder
½ teaspoon salt

8 oz. raw steak
⅛ oz. flour
1 oz. water
2 level teaspoons salt

Make the suet crust pastry and line a pudding basin, leaving sufficient for a lid. Cut the meat into slices and roll in the salted flour. Put into the basin. Add a little water and cover with the remainder of the pastry. Steam for about 2 hours.

572. Beef Stew

8 oz. raw steak
1 carrot, scraped (2 oz.)
1 onion, peeled (2 oz.)
8 oz. water
⅛ oz. flour
2 level teaspoons salt

Cut the meat into pieces and roll in the seasoned flour. Place in a casserole with sliced vegetables and water. Cover and bake in a moderate oven for 2 hours.

573. Curried Meat

9½ oz. cooked meat
2½ oz. dripping
3 onions, peeled (12¾ oz.)
1 apple, peeled and cored (2½ oz.)
2 oz. sultanas
½ oz. desiccated coconut
1 oz. flour
1 oz. curry powder
1 pint water
2 level teaspoons salt

Chop the onions and fry in the dripping. Add the chopped apple, sultanas and coconut, then the flour and curry powder, and fry a minute or two. Add the water and bring to the boil. Simmer for 5 minutes. Add the cooked meat, which has been cut into pieces, and reheat.

574. Fish Cakes

8 oz. steamed cod
4 oz. mashed potato
1 egg
¼ oz. flour
½ oz. margarine
1 oz. dried breadcrumbs
1 level teaspoon salt

Heat the fat in a pan and add the coarsely chopped fish, potato and half the beaten egg. Mix well and allow to cool. Shape into six flat round cakes. Coat with flour, then with the other half of the egg and finally with breadcrumbs. Fry in very hot deep fat for 2 minutes.

575. Fish Cakes (economical)

8 oz. steamed cod
8 oz. mashed potato
½ oz. dried egg powder
1 oz. raw onion
¼ oz. parsley
1 teaspoon vinegar
1 oz. browned breadcrumbs
1 oz. water for reconstituting egg
1 teaspoon salt

Flake the fish and mix with the mashed potato, chopped parsley and onion, salt and vinegar. Shape into cakes and dip in the reconstituted egg and cover with breadcrumbs. Bake in a moderate oven for 30 minutes.

576. Fish Pie

8 oz. steamed cod
4 oz. mashed potato
2 oz. suet
1 egg
7 oz. milk
¾ oz. margarine
¾ oz. breadcrumbs
2 level teaspoons salt

Chop the fish coarsely, and add the suet, potato, half the breadcrumbs and the seasoning Stir in the beaten egg and the milk. Place in a greased pie dish. Cover the surface with breadcrumbs and dabs of margarine. Bake in a moderate oven for about half an hour.

577. Hot Pot

8 oz. raw steak
2 onions, peeled (5 oz.)
2 carrots, scraped (3 oz.)
8 oz. raw potato, peeled
4 oz. water
2 level teaspoons salt

Cut the steak into small pieces and arrange in layers with slices of carrot and onion. Add a little water and seasoning. Slice the potatoes and place on top. Bake in a moderate oven for about 1½ hours.

578. Irish Stew

8 oz. neck of mutton (weighed with bone)
8 oz. potato, peeled
4 oz. onion, peeled
12 oz. water
½ oz. pearl barley
½ teaspoon salt

Cut up the meat, potato and onion and put into a saucepan. Add the water and barley and bring to the boil. Skim well and allow to simmer slowly for 1½ hours.

579. Kedgeree

8 oz. smoked fillet, steamed
2 oz. rice
1 oz. margarine
2 eggs (one hard boiled)
½ teaspoon salt

Boil the rice. Melt the margarine and add the boiled rice, flaked fish, beaten egg and seasoning. Mix well and stir in the chopped hard boiled egg. Put in a pie dish and cook in a moderate oven for 20 minutes.

580 and 581. Sausage Roll

5½ oz. raw flaky pastry
2 oz. raw sausage meat

or

7½ oz. raw short pastry
3½ oz. raw sausage meat

Make the pastry, roll out and cut into squares of 4 inches. Place some sausage in the middle of each. Fold over, and bake in a hot oven for 20–30 minutes.

582 and 583. Sausage Roll (economical)

10 oz. raw short pastry (economical
5 oz. raw sausage meat
¼ oz. flour

or

10 oz. raw potato pastry
5 oz. raw sausage meat
¼ oz. flour

Make the pastry, roll out and cut into squares of 4 inches. Place a piece of sausage meat rolled in flour in the middle of each. Fold over the pastry, and bake in a hot oven for 30 minutes.

584. SHEPHERD'S PIE

6½ oz. beef, cooked
3½ oz. onion, boiled
18½ oz. potato, boiled
2 oz. milk
¾ oz. margarine
6 oz. water
2 level teaspoons salt

Mince the meat and chop up the onion. Moisten with water and add the seasoning. Mash the potatoes with the milk and margarine. Place the mince and onion in a pie dish. Pile the potato on top. Bake in a hot oven till brown.

585. STEAK AND KIDNEY PIE

7 oz. raw flaky pastry
7½ oz. raw beef steak
3½ oz. raw kidney
2 oz. water
2 level teaspoons salt
¼ oz. flour

Make the pastry. Cut the steak and kidney into pieces and roll in flour. Place with water and seasoning in the pie dish. Cover with pastry. Bake in a hot oven for 20 minutes then reduce the heat and continue cooking slowly for 2–2½ hours.

586. TOAD-IN-THE-HOLE

½ pint milk, 4 oz. flour, 2 eggs } Batter
8 oz. raw sausage
2 oz. dripping
2 level teaspoons salt

Make the batter and pour into a pie dish containing hot dripping. Skin the sausages and place them in the batter. Add the salt. Bake in a hot oven for about 40 minutes.

Egg and Cheese Dishes

587. BUCK RAREBIT

3 oz. cheese
1 oz. butter
⅝ oz. milk
2 oz. white toast
¼ oz. butter on toast
1 egg

Grate the cheese and make the toast. Mix together the cheese, butter and milk, and spread evenly on the buttered toast. Place under the grill, and cook until a light brown. Poach the egg, and place on top of the toasted cheese.

588. CHEESE OMELETTE

2 eggs
1½ oz. cheese
¼ oz. butter
1 level teaspoon salt

Beat the eggs with the seasoning and add the grated cheese. Heat the butter in an omelette pan, pour in the mixture and stir till it begins to thicken evenly. While still creamy, fold the omelette in two and brown lightly.

589. CHEESE PUDDING (economical)

1 oz. "Household" milk powder
2 oz. dried egg powder
2 oz. cheese
2 oz. breadcrumbs
11 oz. water for reconstituting egg and milk
1 teaspoon salt
¼ teaspoon mustard

Heat the reconstituted milk to boiling. Add the breadcrumbs, grated cheese, salt and mustard, and stir. Remove from the stove and add the reconstituted beaten eggs. Place in a dish, and brown under the grill for 10 minutes.

590. CHEESE STRAWS

2 oz. flour
2 oz. butter
3 oz. cheese
½ an egg yolk
¼ oz. water
½ teaspoon salt

Rub the butter into the flour. Add the grated cheese and seasoning. Bind to a stiff paste with the yolk and water. Roll out thinly and cut into narrow strips. Bake in a hot oven for about 10 minutes.

591. MACARONI CHEESE

½ pint milk
1 oz. margarine
1 oz. flour
2 oz. macaroni
3 oz. cheese
2 level teaspoons salt

Break the macaroni into small pieces and boil; drain well. Make a sauce of the milk flour and magarine. Stir in three quarters of the grated cheese. Add the boiled macaroni. Put the mixture in a pie dish and sprinkle the remainder of the cheese on top. Brown under the grill.

592. Macaroni Cheese (economical)

3 oz. macaroni
3 oz. cheese
1 oz. flour
¾ oz. margarine
1½ oz. "Household" milk powder
15 oz. water for reconstituting milk
½ teaspoon salt

Boil the macaroni in water until soft, and drain well. Melt the margarine in a saucepan, and stir in the flour and salt. Remove from the stove and add the reconstituted milk slowly. Add the cooked macaroni and about three-quarters of the grated cheese. Pour into a greased dish, and sprinkle the remainder of the cheese on top. Brown under the grill for about 10 minutes.

593. Omelette

2 eggs
1½ oz. butter
½ oz. water
1 level teaspoon salt

Beat the eggs with the salt and add the water. Heat the butter in an omelette pan, pour in the mixture and stir till it begins to thicken evenly. While still creamy, fold the omelette in two and brown lightly.

594. Scotch Egg

3 eggs
8 oz. raw sausage
⅝ oz. breadcrumbs
¼ oz. flour
⅜ oz. beaten egg

Hard boil the eggs, cool and remove shells. Skin the sausages and flatten each on a floured board. Dip each egg in flour and cover with the sausage meat. Brush with beaten egg and coat with crumbs. Fry in very hot deep fat for about 3 minutes.

595. Scrambled Eggs

2 eggs
¾ oz. butter
½ oz. milk
1 level teaspoon salt

Beat the eggs with the seasoning and add the milk. Heat the butter in a pan and add the beaten eggs and milk. Stir over a gentle heat until the mixture thickens.

596. Scrambled Eggs (with Dried Eggs)

½ oz. dried egg powder
¼ oz. margarine
1 oz. water for reconstituting the egg
½ level teaspoon salt

Melt the margarine in a saucepan and add the beaten reconstituted egg and salt. Stir over a gentle heat until the mixture thickens.

597. Welsh Rarebit

3 oz. cheese
1 oz. butter
⅝ oz. milk
2 oz. white toast
¼ oz. butter on toast

Make as for Buck Rarebit, omitting the egg.

Sauces and Soups

598. Bread Sauce

½ pint milk
2 oz. fresh breadcrumbs
¼ oz. butter
1 small onion
½ teaspoon salt

Put the milk and onion in a saucepan and bring to the boil. Add the breadcrumbs, and simmer gently for about 20 minutes. Remove the onion and add the seasoning, stir in the butter and serve.

601. Cheese Sauce

½ pint milk, ¾ oz. flour, ¾ oz. margarine } White sauce
1½ oz. cheese
1 level teaspoon salt

Melt the fat in a pan. Add the flour, and cook gently for a few minutes, stirring all the time. Add the milk, and cook until the mixture thickens, stirring continually. Add the grated cheese and seasoning. Cook for a few minutes.

602. Egg Sauce

½ pint milk, ¾ oz. flour, ¾ oz. margarine } White sauce
1 hard-boiled egg
1 level teaspoon salt

Make the sauce and add the chopped egg and seasoning.

603. Onion Sauce

½ pint milk, ¾ oz. flour, ¾ oz. margarine } White sauce
8 oz. onion, boiled
1 level teaspoon salt

Make the sauce and add the chopped onion and seasoning.

604. Potato Soup

13¼ oz. potatoes, peeled
1 onion, peeled (4¾ oz.)
1 oz. dripping
½ pint milk
½ pint water
2 level teaspoons salt

Melt the fat in a pan. Slice the vegetables and fry in the fat. Add the water and seasoning. Bring to the boil, cover and simmer for an hour. Rub through a sieve, add the milk and reheat.

606. White Sauce, Savoury

½ pint milk
¾ oz. flour
¾ oz. margarine
1 level teaspoon salt

Melt the fat in a pan. Add the flour, and cook for a few minutes, stirring all the time Add the milk and seasoning, and cook gently until the mixture thickens, stirring continually

607. White Sauce, Sweet

½ pint milk
¾ oz. flour
¾ oz. margarine
1 oz. sugar

Make the sauce in the same way as the savoury sauce, adding the sugar instead of salt.

Vegetable Dishes

608. Potato Cakes (economical)

8 oz. mashed potato
1½ oz. flour
1 level teaspoon salt

Mix the flour and salt with the mashed potato. Roll out, cut into cakes and cook slowly on a hot plate or girdle.

609. Vegetable Pie with Potato Pastry (economical)

12½ oz. raw potato
5½ oz. raw turnip
4¼ oz. raw carrot
1¼ oz. raw onion
7¼ oz. raw potato pastry
3½ oz. water
1 teaspoon salt

Slice the vegetables and place in a pie dish. Add the salt and water, and cover with the pastry. Bake in a moderate oven for 1 hour.

COMPOSITION OF FOODS

PER 100 GRAMMES

Cereals and Cereal Foods

No.	Food.	Description and number of samples.	g. per 100 g. Water.	Sugar (as invert sugar).	Starch and dextrins (as glucose).	Total nitrogen.
1	All-Bran, Kellogg's	2 packets from different shops	8·0	18·2	39·8	2·20
2	Arrowroot	2 samples from different shops	12·2	Tr.	94·0	0·07
3	Barley, pearl, raw	2 samples from different shops	10·6	Tr.	83·6	1·35
4	Barley, pearl, boiled	2 samples from different shops (boiled in water)	69·6	Tr.	27·6	0·46
5	Biscuits, cream crackers	2 varieties	3·5	Tr.	57·5	1·49
6	Biscuits, digestive (1935)	3 varieties	4·5	16·4	49·6	1·68
7	Biscuits, digestive (1944)	Same 3 varieties	5·2	16·3	50·3	1·30
8	Biscuits, plain mixed (1936)	Marie (3 varieties), Osborne (3 varieties)	5·2	15·8	59·5	1·29
9	Biscuits, plain mixed (1944)	Marie (1 variety), Osborne (2 varieties), Petit Beurre (1 variety).	5·1	19·9	54·5	1·23
10	Biscuits, rusks	2 varieties	6·4	11·8	69·8	1·06
11	Biscuits, sweet mixed	3 varieties	0·7	25·0	41·5	0·97
12	Biscuits, water	3 varieties	4·5	2·3	73·5	1·89
13	Bread, currant (1936)	4 samples from different shops	37·7	13·0	38·8	1·12
14	Bread, Hovis (1936)	4 samples from different shops	39·0	Tr.	46·7	1·83
15	Bread, malt (1936)	3 varieties	39·0	18·6	30·8	1·46
16	Bread, brown (90%)	Baked from flours Nos. 37–40. (See p. 28.)	39·0	Tr.	53·3	1·46
17	Bread, National Wheatmeal (85%)	Baked from flours Nos. 37–40. (See p. 28.)	38·0	Tr.	55·5	1·48
18	Bread (80%)	Baked from flours Nos. 37–40. (See p. 28.)	37·0	Tr.	57·5	1·46
19	Bread, white (70%)	Baked from flours Nos. 37–40. (See p. 28.)	36·0	Tr.	59·3	1·43
20	Bread, white, toasted	Baked from flours Nos. 37–40. (See p. 28.)	24·0	Tr.	70·5	1·70
21	Bread, white, fried in lard	Baked from flours Nos. 37–40. (See p. 28.)	4·0	Tr.	52·5	1·27
22	Cornflakes, Kellogg's	2 packets from different shops	8·0	10·4	77·8	1·16
23	Cornflour	3 samples from different shops	12·5	Tr.	92·0	0·09
24	Custard powder	Take as cornflour				

Cereals and Cereal Foods—*continued*

No.	Food.	g. per 100 g.			Calories per 100 g.	mg. per 100 g.									Acid-base balance, c.c. per 100 g.	
		Protein (N × 5·7).	Fat.	Available carbohydrate (as monosaccharides).		Na.	K.	Ca.	Mg.	Fe.	Cu.	P.	S.	Cl.	$\frac{N}{10}$ Acid.	$\frac{N}{10}$ Alkali.
1	All-Bran, Kellogg's ..	12·6	4·5	58·0	311	(1210)	955	82·1	420·1	10·80	0·46	815	182·0	(2020)	43	
2	Arrowroot	0·4	0·1	94·0	355	4·8	18	7·0	7·8	1·95	0·22	27	1·6	7·1	4	
3	Barley, pearl, raw ..	7·7	1·7	83·6	360	2·6	123	9·7	20·2	0·67	0·12	206	107·0	105·0	175	
4	Barley, pearl, boiled ..	2·6	0·6	27·6	120	0·8	40	3·4	6·8	0·23	0·04	70	36·5	35·8	60	
5	Biscuits, cream crackers	8·5	33·0	57·5	557	(438)	128	17·9	19·0	0·96	0·15	82	77·8	(705)	53	
6	Biscuits, digestive (1935)	9·6	20·5	66·0	481	(435)	156	43·6	32·0	1·57	0·23	134	72·0	(432)		24
7	Biscuits, digestive (1944)	7·4	22·6	66·6	489	(432)	180	35·6	40·2	2·00	0·30	148	—	(375)	—	—
8	Biscuits, plain mixed (1936)	7·4	13·2	75·3	435	(244)	170	45·4	14·3	1·24	0·08	41	83·4	(260)		33
9	Biscuits, plain mixed (1944)	7·0	15·5	74.4	451	(441)	185	53·6	41·4	1·81	0·27	183	—	(335)	—	—
10	Biscuits, rusks	6·0	8·4	81·6	409	(206)	140	86·6	27·3	2·66	0·21	81	107·0	(174)		24
11	Biscuits, sweet mixed ..	5·5	30·7	66·5	556	(216)	136	27·2	14·0	0·83	0·12	66	31·8	(371)	13	
12	Biscuits, water	10·7	12·5	75·8	444	(472)	142	22·1	18·9	0·94	0·08	87	100·0	(678)	40	
13	Bread, currant (1936) ..	6·4	3·4	51·8	252	(164)	250	37·6	24·7	2·35	0·09	121	59·4	(284)	20	
14	Bread, Hovis (1936) ..	10·4	3·7	46·7	252	(455)	243	27·5	78·8	2·95	0·09	257	77·3	(640)	55	
15	Bread, malt (1936) ..	8·3	3·3	49·4	250	(275)	381	53·0	77·8	3·21	0·06	253	114·5	(526)	74	
16	Bread, brown (90%) ..	8·3	1·4	53·3	246	(393)	147	17·2	52·3	2·01	0·32	160	—	(607)	—	—
17	Bread, National Wheatmeal (85%).	8·5	1·2	55·5	254	(393)	116	15·3	37·4	1·83	0·26	127	—	(607)	—	—
18	Bread (80%)	8·3	1·0	57·5	259	(393)	94	13·2	26·9	1·59	0·20	98	—	(607)	—	—
19	Bread, white (70%) ..	8·1	0·8	59·3	264	(393)	70	11·4	16·4	1·43	0·15	69	—	(607)	—	—
20	Bread, white, toasted ..	9·6	1·0	70·5	314	(467)	83	13·5	19·5	1·70	0·18	82	—	(720)	—	—
21	Bread, white, fried ..	7·2	37·2	52·5	573	(348)	62	10·1	14·5	1·27	0·13	61	—	(537)	—	—
22	Cornflakes, Kellogg's ..	6·6	0·8	88·2	367	(1050)	114	7·4	16·5	2·80	0·09	58	92·5	(1520)	20	
23	Cornflour	0·5	0·7	92·0	354	51·6	61	15·3	7·2	1·43	0·13	39	1·1	71·0		6
24	Custard powder ..							Take as Cornflour.								

Note.—If flour is fortified with $CaCO_3$, add 46 mg. Ca per 100 g. bread.

Cereals and Cereal Foods—*continued*

No.	Food.	Description and number of samples.	g. per 100 g.			
			Water.	*Sugar (as invert sugar).*	*Starch and dextrins (as glucose).*	*Total nitrogen.*
25	Flour, English (100% whole wheat)	Composite sample of 19 varieties, weighted for popularity. (See *Biochem, J.*, 1945. **39,** 213.)	15·0	Tr.	73·4	1·56
26	Flour, English (85%) ..		15·0	Tr.	79·1	1·50
27	Flour, English (80%)		15·0	Tr.	80·8	1·44
28	Flour, English (75%)		15·0	Tr.	81·5	1·40
29	Flour, English (70%)		15·0	Tr.	81·9	1·39
30	Flour, English (Patent)		15·0	Tr.	83·2	1·34
31	Flour, Manitoba (100% whole wheat)	Composite sample from 24 shiploads (12 No. 1 Manitoba and 12 No. 2 Manitoba). (See *Biochem, J.*, 1945. **39,** 213.)	15·0	Tr.	69·1	2·39
32	Flour, Manitoba (85%) ..		15·0	Tr.	75·0	2·38
33	Flour, Manitoba (80%)		15·0	Tr.	75·5	2·32
34	Flour, Manitoba (75%)		15·0	Tr.	76·3	2·29
35	Flour, Manitoba (70%)		15·0	Tr.	76·9	2·24
36	Flour, Manitoba (Patent) ..		15·0	Tr.	78·2	2·07
37	Flour, mixed grist, brown (90%)	Milled from a mixed grist consisting of 60 parts Manitoba wheat : 40 parts English wheat from the composite samples shown above.	15·0	Tr.	74·2	2·03
38	Flour, mixed grist, National Wheatmeal (85%)		15·0	Tr.	76·0	2·03
39	Flour, mixed grist (80%) ..		15·0	Tr.	77·6	1·97
40	Flour, mixed grist, white (70%)		15·0	Tr.	78·9	1·90
41	Force	2 packets from different shops	8·5	7·0	76·7	1·63
42	Grapenuts	2 packets from different shops	8·0	11·9	63·3	2·05
43	Macaroni (1936), raw	2 samples from different shops	12·4	Tr.	79·2	1·87
44	Macaroni (1936), boiled	2 samples from different shops (boiled in water) ..	72·2	Tr.	25·2	0·58
45	Macaroni (1943), raw	6 samples from different shops	12·6	Tr.	77·8	2·06

Cereals and Cereal Foods—*continued*

No.	Food.	g. per 100 g.			Calories per 100 g.	mg. per 100 g.									Acid-base balance, c.c. per 100 g.	
		Protein (N × 5·7).	Fat.	Available carbohydrate (as monosaccharides).		Na.	K.	Ca.	Mg.	Fe.	Cu.	P.	S.	Cl.	$\frac{N}{10}$ Acid.	$\frac{N}{10}$ Alkali.
25	Flour, English (100%) ..	8·9	2·2	73·4	333	3·4	361	35·5	106·0	3·05	0·65	340	—	35·5	—	—
26	Flour, English (85%) ..	8·6	1·5	79·1	346	2·9	179	24·5	35·0	2·22	0·36	153	—	42·2	—	—
27	Flour, English (80%) ..	8·2	1·3	80·8	348	2·1	151	21·5	24·0	1·65	0·27	118	—	44·4	—	—
28	Flour, English (75%) ..	8·0	1·1	81·5	349	2·2	118	19·2	16·8	1·35	0·22	93	—	44·9	—	—
29	Flour, English (70%) ..	7·9	1·0	81·9	349	2·1	111	18·9	13·9	1·40	0·22	84	—	45·0	—	—
30	Flour, English (Patent)	7·6	0·8	83·2	352	—	99	15·2	8·7	0·95	0·20	68	—	41·5	—	—
31	Flour, Manitoba (100%)	13·6	2·5	69·1	339	3·2	312	27·6	141·0	3·81	0·60	350	—	38·5	—	—
32	Flour, Manitoba (85%)	13·6	1·7	74·0	350	4·1	146	18·5	61·8	2·70	0·34	188	—	44·5	—	—
33	Flour, Manitoba (80%)	13·2	1·4	75·5	350	2·9	112	15·4	44·6	2·47	0·27	139	—	48·5	—	—
34	Flour, Manitoba (75%)	13·1	1·3	76·3	353	—	87	13·1	30·4	2·27	0·22	109	—	48·0	—	—
35	Flour, Manitoba (70%)	12·8	1·2	76·9	352	2·2	82	12·8	26·9	2·23	0·18	97	—	47·8	—	—
36	Flour, Manitoba (Patent)	11·8	0·9	78·2	351	1·8	71	11·1	21·5	2·08	0·15	82	—	45·0	—	—
37	Flour, mixed grist, brown (90%)	11·6	1·9	74·2	343	3·5	205	24·0	73·0	2·80	0·44	223	—	41·0	—	—
38	Flour, mixed grist, National Wheatmeal (85%)	11·6	1·6	76·0	348	3·6	159	20·9	51·1	2·50	0·35	174	—	43·6	—	—
39	Flour, mixed grist (80%)	11·2	1·4	77·6	350	2·6	127	17·8	36·4	2·15	0·27	132	—	46·9	—	—
40	Flour, mixed grist, white (70%)	10·8	1·1	78·9	350	2·1	93	15·2	21·7	1·90	0·20	92	—	46·7	—	—
41	Force	9·3	1·9	83·7	370	(692)	405	66·3	148·0	3·98	0·36	339	104·0	(1120)	38	
42	Grapenuts	11·7	3·0	75·2	358	(658)	423	47·8	153·0	5·64	0·19	333	144·0	(905)	14	
43	Macaroni (1936), raw ..	10·7	2·0	97·2	360	25·6	217	26·3	57·3	1·43	0·07	152	95·0	31·4	38	
44	Macaroni (1936), boiled	3·4	0·6	25·2	114	7·9	67	8·1	17·6	0·45	0·02	47	29·4	9·7	12	
45	Macaroni (1943), raw ..	11·7	1·3	77·8	352	(160)	139	20·3	41·7	1·30	0·30	141	—	(153)	—	—

Note.—If flour is fortified with $CaCO_3$, add 63 mg. Ca per 100 g. flour.

Cereals and Cereal Foods—*continued*

No.	Food.	Description and number of samples.	*g. per 100 g.* Water.	Sugar (as invert sugar).	Starch and dextrins (as glucose).	Total nitrogen.
46	Oatmeal, raw	Coarse, medium and fine. Two samples of each from different shops.	8·9	Tr.	72·8	2·12
47	Oatmeal porridge	2½ oz. mixed sample and 2 level teaspoons salt per pint of water.	89·1	Tr.	8·2	0·24
48	Post Toasties	2 packets from different shops	8·0	10·2	78·8	1·16
49	Rice, polished, raw	5 samples from different shops	11·7	Tr.	86·8	1·09
50	Rice, polished, boiled	5 samples from different shops (boiled in water)	69·9	Tr.	29·6	0·37
51	Rye (100%)	Commercial grist of all-English rye.	15·0	Tr.	75·9	1·40
52	Rye (85%)	Commercial grist of all-English rye.	15·0	Tr.	80·2	1·28
53	Rye (75%)	Commercial grist of all-English rye.	15·0	Tr.	82·5	1·17
54	Rye (60%)	Commercial grist of all-English rye.	15·0	Tr.	85·8	0·99
55	Ryvita	12 packets from different shops	5·9	Tr.	86·8	1·19
56	Sago	2 samples from different shops	12·6	Tr.	94·0	0·04
57	Semolina	2 samples from different shops (coarse and fine)	14·0	Tr.	77·5	1·87
58	Shredded Wheat	2 packets from different shops	8·0	Tr.	79·0	1·69
59	Soya. Full fat flour	Mixed sample, supplied by the Cereals Research Station.	7·0	Tr.	13·3	6·45
60	Soya. Low fat flour or grits	Mixed sample, supplied by the Cereals Research Station.	7·0	Tr.	17·2	7·94
61	Tapioca	4 varieties (medium pearl, seed pearl, coarse and flake)	12·2	Tr.	95·0	0·07
62	Vita-Weat	12 packets from different shops	4·9	Tr.	77·8	1·50

Cereals and Cereal Foods—*continued*

No.	Food.	g. per 100 g. Protein (N × 5·7).	Fat.	Available carbohydrate (as monosaccharides).	Calories per 100 g.	mg. per 100 g. Na.	K.	Ca.	Mg.	Fe.	Cu.	P.	S.	Cl.	Acid-base balance, c.c. per 100 g. $\frac{N}{10}$ Acid.	$\frac{N}{10}$ Alkali.
46	Oatmeal, raw	12·1	8·7	72·8	404	33·4	368	55·3	113·0	4·12	0·23	380	155·0	73·0	132	
47	Oatmeal porridge ..	1·4	0·9	8·2	45	(578)	42	6·3	12·7	0·47	0·03	43	17·7	(890)	15	
48	Post Toasties	6·6	0·6	89·0	367	(810)	120	4·7	16·7	1·67	0·15	54	83·0	(1210)	29	
49	Rice, polished, raw ..	6·2	1·0	86·8	361	6·3	113	3·7	13·1	0·45	0·06	99	78·5	27·0	76	
50	Rice, polished, boiled ..	2·1	0·3	29·6	122	2·2	38	1·3	4·4	0·16	0·02	34	26·8	9·2	26	
51	Rye (100%)	8·0	2·0	75·9	335	—	412	31·5	92·0	2·70	—	359	—	—	—	—
52	Rye (85%)	7·3	1·6	80·2	347	—	203	26·1	45·0	1·97	—	193	—	—	—	—
53	Rye (75%)	6·7	1·3	82·5	350	—	172	19·5	26·0	1·72	—	129	—	—	—	—
54	Rye (60%)	5·6	1·0	85·8	354	—	140	15·3	16·0	1·32	—	78	—	—	—	—
55	Ryvita	6·8	2·1	86·8	373	(615)	469	40·5	90·7	3·73	0·15	295	87·0	(935)	25	
56	Sago	0·2	0·2	94·0	355	3·4	5	9·8	2·5	1·18	0·03	29	0·5	12·8	13	
57	Semolina	10·7	1·8	77·5	352	11·8	166	18·2	32·0	1·04	0·15	114	91·8	71·0	67	
58	Shredded Wheat ..	9·7	2·8	79·0	362	16·5	303	34·8	120·0	4·48	0·45	287	86·5	71·0	57	
59	Soya. Full fat flour ..	40·3*	23·5	13·3†	433	—	1660	208·0	235·0	6·93	—	597	—	—	—	—
60	Soya. Low fat flour or grits.	49·6*	7·2	17·2†	335	—	2025	241·0	286·0	9·14	—	643	—	—	—	—
61	Tapioca	0·4	0·1	95·0	359	4·2	20	8·2	2·0	0·32	0·07	30	3·5	13·1	12	
62	Vita-Weat	8·6	10·3	77·8	423	(605)	430	44·0	118·0	3·40	0·19	372	93·2	(845)	43	

* Total N × 6·25. † 75 per cent. total carbohydrate taken to be available.

Dairy Products

No.	Food.	Description and number of samples.	g. per 100 g.	
			Water.	*Total nitrogen.*
63	Butter, fresh	6 samples from different shops (Foreign, Empire and English)	13·9	0·07
64	Cheese, Cheddar	6 samples from different shops	37·0	3·98
65	Cheese, cream (home-made)	1 sample only	10·0	0·51
66	Cheese, Dutch	5 samples from different shops	46·3	4·51
67	Cheese, Gorgonzola	4 samples from different shops	41·0	3·97
68	Cheese, Gruyère	4 samples from different shops	21·9	5·90
69	Cheese, packet	6 varieties	43·0	3·60
70	Cheese, Parmesan	3 samples from different shops	28·0	5·50
71	Cheese, St. Ivel	8 samples from different shops	45·7	3·70
72	Cheese, Stilton	3 samples from different shops	28·2	4·02
73	Cream	Various	53·0	0·28
74	Egg white	34 eggs, English and Danish, from different shops	88·3	1·44
75	Egg yolk	34 eggs, English and Danish, from different shops	51·0	2·58
76	Eggs, raw or boiled	34 eggs, English and Danish, from different shops	73·4	1·90
77	Eggs, dried	Packets from 6 different shops	7·0	6·97
78	Eggs, fried	6 eggs from different shops	63·3	2·26
79	Eggs, poached	6 eggs from different shops	74·7	1·99
80	Milk, fresh, whole	8 samples from different dairies	87·0	0·53
81	Milk, fresh, skimmed	Calculated on the assumption that skimmed milk contains 0·2 per cent. of fat	90·2	0·55
82	Milk, condensed, whole, sweetened	3 varieties	20·3	1·28
83	Milk, condensed, whole, unsweetened	3 varieties	68·3	1·22
84	Milk, condensed, skimmed, sweetened	2 varieties	27·0	1·55
85	Milk, dried, skimmed ("Household")	Tins from 5 different shops	5·0	5·46
86	Milk, dried, whole	Calculated on the assumption that dried milk is 8 times as concentrated as fresh milk. The figures for iron and copper may vary with the method of manufacture.	1·3	4·24

Dairy Products—*continued*

No.	Food.	g. per 100 g. Protein (N × 6·25).	Fat.	Available carbohydrate (as monosaccharides).	Calories per 100 g.	mg. per 100 g. Na.	K.	Ca.	Mg.	Fe.	Cu.	P.	S.	Cl.	Acid-base balance, c.c. per 100 g. $\frac{N}{10}$ Acid.	$\frac{N}{10}$ Alkali.
63	Butter, fresh	0·4	85·1	Tr.	793	(223)	15	14·8	2·4	0·16	0·03	24	9	(332)	4	
64	Cheese, Cheddar ..	24·9	34·5	Tr.	423	(612)	116	810·0	46·9	0·57	0·03	545	230	(1060)	54	
65	Cheese, cream	3·2	86·0	Tr.	813	(110)	47	29·6	5·2	0·14	0·04	44	64	(151)	34	
66	Cheese, Dutch	28·1	16·8	Tr.	271	(1250)	96	900·0	52·6	0·78	0·05	478	187	(2050)		59
67	Cheese, Gorgonzola ..	24·8	31·1	Tr.	392	(1220)	172	540·0	37·8	0·50	0·15	375	177	(1800)	3	
68	Cheese, Gruyère.. ..	36·8	33·4	Tr.	461	(542)	128	1080·0	45·0	0·26	0·27	698	206	(825)		36
69	Cheese, packet	22·5	30·1	Tr.	372	(918)	86	724·0	47·6	0·57	0·03	480	321	(1080)		5
70	Cheese, Parmesan ..	34·4	29·7	Tr.	417	(755)	153	1220·0	49·6	0·37	0·36	772	251	(1110)		51
71	Cheese, St. Ivel	23·1	30·5	Tr.	379	(567)	68	483·0	23·2	0·72	0·02	375	186	(910)	89	
72	Cheese, Stilton	25·1	40·0	Tr.	475	(1150)	161	362·0	27·2	0·46	0·03	304	228	(1720)	78	
73	Cream	1·8	42·0	2·4	406	31·5	93	59·2	4·5	0·23	0·15	25	33	54·0		19
74	Egg white	9·0	Tr.	0·0	37	192·0	148	5·2	10·7	0·10	0·03	33	183	170·0	50	
75	Egg yolk	16·2	30·5	0·0	350	50·0	123	131·5	14·9	6·13	0·02	495	165	142·0	332	
76	Eggs, raw or boiled ..	11·9	12·3	0·0	163	135·0	138	56·0	12·3	2·53	0·03	218	173	159·0	162	
77	Eggs, dried	43·4	43·3	0·0	580	519·0	483	190·0	41·4	7·85	0·18	799	630	592·0	598	
78	Eggs, fried	14·1	19·5	0·0	239	220·0	176	64·2	13·9	2·53	0·05	256	206	199·0	165	
79	Eggs, poached	12·4	11·7	0·0	160	111·0	118	51·8	11·2	2·30	0·03	239	181	155·0	197	
80	Milk, fresh whole ..	3·3	3·7	*4·8	66	50·0	160	120·0	14·0	0·08	0·02	95	29	98·0		27
81	Milk, fresh skimmed ..	3·4	0·2	*5·1	35	52·0	166	124·0	14·5	0·08	0·02	98	30	102·0		29
82	Milk, condensed, whole, sweetened	8·0	12·0	56·0	354	143·0	408	344·0	36·0	0·17	0·08	238	83	284·0		84
83	Milk, condensed, whole, unsweetened	7·6	8·4	*12·3	155	161·0	502	290·0	34·8	0·18	0·11	254	75	277·0		84
84	Milk, condensed, skimmed, sweetened	9·7	0·3	60·0	267	180·0	498	384·0	37·7	0·29	0·03	270	94	310·0		109
85	Milk, dried, skimmed ("Household")	34·0	0·3	*49·2	326	600·0	1335	1265·0	111·0	0·52	1·39†	1050	300	1130·0		145
86	Milk, dried whole ..	26·4	29·7	*38·8	530	400·0	1280	960·0	112·0	0·64	0·16	760	234	784·0		216

* See p. 6. † Most of this copper was probably derived from the manufacturing machinery. See p. 9.

Meat, Poultry and Game

No.	Food.	Method of cooking.	Nature of edible (analysed) material.	Edible matter, as eaten, expressed as a percentage of the weight as purchased.	g. per 100 g.		
					Water.	*Total nitrogen.*	*Purine nitrogen.*
87	*Bacon, Danish Wilts., tank cured	Raw..	Average of 6 medium lean sides (rind and bone excluded)	—	46·9	2·23	0·037
88	*Bacon, Danish Wilts., tank cured	Raw..	Fore ends of above sides (26·6 per cent. of total) (rind and bone excluded)	—	51·2	2·35	0·039
89	*Bacon, Danish Wilts., tank cured	Raw..	Middle of above sides (50·6 per cent. of total) (rind and bone excluded)	—	40·9	2·07	0·035
90	*Bacon, Danish Wilts., tank cured	Raw..	Gammon of above sides (22·8 per cent. of total) (rind and bone excluded)	—	55·4	2·45	0·041
91	*Bacon, English Wilts., dry cured	Raw..	Average of 3 sides (rind and bone excluded)	—	36·3	2·00	0·034
92	*Bacon, English Midland, dry cured	Raw..	Average of 3 sides (rind and bone excluded)	—	25·3	1·67	0·028
93	Bacon, back	Rashers fried	Fat and lean	48	12·7	4·12	0·069
94	Bacon, collar	Rashers fried	Fat and lean	50	27·3	4·58	0·080
95	Bacon, gammon	Rashers fried	Fat and lean	58	24·9	5·28	0·086
96	Bacon, streaky	Rashers fried	Fat and lean	41	20·0	3·99	0·066
97	Beef, corned	Tinned	All	100	58·5	3·60	0·036
98	Beef, frozen (Argentine, N.Z., Australia, S. Africa)	Raw..	All	—	70·3	3·40	0·050
99	Beef, silverside	Boiled	All	74	46·2	4·62	0·055
100	Beef, sirloin	Roast (underdone in centre)	Lean only	44	58·4	4·47	0·060
101	Beef, sirloin	Roast (underdone in centre)	All except bone	60	45·2	3·54	0·046

* These bacons were green, *i.e.*, unsmoked. About 5 per cent. of the total weight is lost on smoking.

Meat, Poultry and Game—*continued*

No.	Food.	g. per 100 g.			Calories per 100 g.	mg. per 100 g.									Acid-base balance, c.c. per 100 g.	
		Protein.	Fat.	Carbohydrate (as glucose).		Na.	K.	Ca.	Mg.	Fe.	Cu.	P.	S.	Cl.	$\frac{N}{10}$ Acid.	$\frac{N}{10}$ Alkali.
	Bacon, raw															
87	Danish Wilts., average	14·0	37·4	0·0	405	(1220)	250	13·5	14·5	1·3	0·19	122	162	(1870)	75	
88	Danish Wilts., fore end	14·7	31·7	0·0	355	(1350)	265	14·4	15·5	1·1	0·20	138	170	(2070)	107	
89	Danish Wilts., middle..	13·0	44·6	0·0	468	(1160)	227	13·5	13·8	1·3	0·19	119	150	(1760)	48	
90	Danish Wilts., gammon	15·3	28·2	0·0	325	(1200)	285	12·6	14·8	1·7	0·17	111	178	(1880)	98	
91	English Wilts.	12·5	49·3	0·0	509	(975)	268	13·5	12·3	0·9	0·27	94	145	(1510)	67	
92	English Midland ..	10·4	61·1	0·0	612	(830)	281	7·2	10·4	1·0	0·26	92	121	(1300)	58	
93	Bacon, back, fried ..	24·6	53·4	0·0	597	(2790)	517	11·5	25·7	2·8	—	229	298	(4150)	129	
94	Bacon, collar, fried ..	27·4	35·0	0·0	438	(3050)	492	23·2	25·8	3·9	—	236	332	(4790)	226	
95	Bacon, gammon, fried ..	31·3	33·9	0·0	444	(2330)	638	24·9	32·7	2·8	—	303	383	(4210)	408	
96	Bacon, streaky, fried ..	24·0	46·0	0·0	526	(3090)	462	52·3	25·1	3·2	—	238	299	(4750)	170	
97	Beef, corned	22·3	15·0	0·0	231	(1380)	117	12·8	29·0	9·8	—	119	212	(2080)	137	
98	Beef, frozen raw ..	20·3	7·3	0·0	151	74	350	8·0	25·0	3·7	0·16	200	215	74	137	
99	Beef, silverside, boiled ..	28·0	20·0	0·0	301	(1470)	288	23·3	20·0	3·7	0·19	243	292	(2320)	252	
100	Beef, sirloin, roast, lean only.	26·8	12·3	0·0	224	70	357	6·5	25·0	5·3	0·19	284	283	74	235	
101	Beef, sirloin, roast, lean and fat.	21·3	32·1	0·0	385	62	290	5·8	19·9	4·6	0·17	237	224	64	190	

Meat, Poultry and Game—*continued*

No.	Food.	Method of cooking.	Nature of edible (analysed) material.	Edible matter, as eaten, expressed as a percentage of the weight as purchased.	g. per 100 g.		
					Water.	*Total nitrogen.*	*Purine nitrogen.*
102	Beef, steak	Raw	Lean only	—	68·3	3·19	0·058
103	Beef, steak	Fried (lightly cooked)	Lean with some fat	81	56·9	3·42	0·061
104	Beef, steak	Grilled	All	73	50·5	4·24	0·085
105	Beef, steak	Stewed 4 hours	Lean only	57	58·1	5·19	0·061
106	Beef, topside	Boiled	Lean only	59	56·6	5·44	0·072
107	Beef, topside	Roast	Lean only	79	56·2	4·40	0·073
108	Beef, topside	Roast	All	89	50·0	3·99	0·066
109	Brain, calf	Boiled 10–15 min.	All	90	80·2	1·96	0·040
110	Brain, sheep	Boiled	All	95	79·7	1·92	0·031
111	Chicken	Boiled	Flesh only	48	61·0	4·37	0·061
111*a*	Chicken (weighed with bone)	Boiled	Flesh only	48	39·6	2·85	0·040
112	Chicken	Roast (with basting)	Flesh only	40	61·1	4·84	0·072
112*a*	Chicken (weighed with bone)	Roast (with basting)	Flesh only	40	33·0	2·61	0·039
113	Dripping, beef	Analysed as purchased	All	100	1·0	Tr.	—
114	Duck	Roast (with basting)	Flesh only	42	52·0	3·67	0·064
114*a*	Duck (weighed with bone)	Roast (with basting)	Flesh only	42	28·1	1·98	0·035
115	Goose	Roast (with basting)	Flesh only	39	46·7	4·69	0·100
115*a*	Goose (weighed with bone)	Roast (with basting)	Flesh only	39	27·1	2·72	0·058
116	Grouse	Roast (with basting)	Flesh only	51	61·6	5·00	0·098
116*a*	Grouse (weighed with bone)	Roast (with basting)	Flesh only	51	40·6	3·30	0·065

Meat, Poultry and Game—*continued*

No.	Food.	g. per 100 g.			Calories per 100 g.	mg. per 100 g.									Acid-base balance, c.c. per 100 g.	
		Protein.	Fat.	Carbohydrate (as glucose).		Na.	K.	Ca.	Mg.	Fe.	Cu.	P.	S.	Cl.	$\frac{N}{10}$ Acid.	$\frac{N}{10}$ Alkali.
102	Beef steak, raw	19·3	10·5	0·0	177	69	334	5·4	24·5	4·3	—	276	202	70	185	
103	Beef steak, fried ..	20·4	20·4	0·0	273	80	371	5·2	24·8	6·0	—	257	216	90	173	
104	Beef steak, grilled ..	25·2	21·6	0·0	304	67	368	9·2	25·2	5·2	—	303	268	64	232	
105	Beef steak, stewed ..	30·8	8·6	0·0	206	38	153	3·0	21·1	5·1	—	229	328	39	289	
106	Beef, topside, boiled ..	33·3	8·2	0·0	213	46	220	3·6	25·9	8·3	—	247	345	49	289	
107	Beef, topside, roast, lean only	26·7	15·0	0·0	249	76	370	6·2	28·1	4·7	0·25	286	279	62	222	
108	Beef, topside, roast, lean and fat	24·2	23·8	0·0	321	72	337	5·9	25·4	4·4	0·23	264	252	59	204	
109	Brain, calf, boiled ..	12·0	5·8	0·0	103	147	270	16·0	13·3	2·0	—	355	132	167	207	
110	Brain, sheep, boiled ..	11·7	6·7	0·0	110	170	268	10·8	17·8	2·2	—	339	129	144	177	
111	Chicken, boiled	26·2	10·3	0·0	203	98	381	10·7	26·4	2·1	—	270	293	62	207	
111*a*	Chicken, boiled (weighed with bone)	17·0	6·7	0·0	132	64	248	7·0	17·2	1·4	—	175	190	40	135	
112	Chicken, roast	29·6	7·3	0·0	189	80	355	14·5	23·0	2·6	—	271	324	100	254	
112*a*	Chicken, roast (weighed with bone)	16·0	3·9	0·0	102	43	192	7·8	12·4	1·4	—	146	175	54	137	
113	Dripping, beef	Tr.	99·0	0·0	921	5	4	0·8	Tr.	0·2	—	13	9	2	11	
114	Duck, roast	22·8	23·6	0·0	313	195	319	19·0	23·9	5·8	—	231	395	158	244	
114*a*	Duck, roast (weighed with bone)	12·3	12·8	0·0	169	105	172	10·2	12·9	3·1	—	125	213	85	132	
115	Goose, roast	28·0	22·4	0·0	323	145	406	10·4	30·8	4·6	—	267	319	159	218	
115*a*	Goose, roast (weighed with bone)	16·2	13·0	0·0	187	84	236	6·0	17·8	2·7	—	155	185	92	127	
116	Grouse, roast	30·1	5·3	0·0	173	96	466	29·8	40·6	7·6	—	338	340	134	258	
116*a*	Grouse, roast (weighed with bone)	20·0	3·5	0·0	114	63	308	19·6	26·8	5·0	—	223	224	88	170	

Meat, Poultry and Game—*continued*

No.	Food.	Method of cooking.	Nature of edible (analysed) material.	Edible matter, as eaten, expressed as a percentage of the weight as purchased.	g. per 100 g. Water.	Total nitrogen.	Purine nitrogen.
117	Guinea-fowl	Roast (with basting)	Flesh only	41	56·9	5·32	0·142
117*a*	Guinea-fowl (weighed with bone)	Roast (with basting)	Flesh only	41	30·1	2·83	0·075
118	Ham, York	Raw	Average of 3 hams (all except bone)	—	31·0	2·40	—
119	Ham	Boiled (purchased cooked and sliced)	Lean only	67	55·8	3·86	0·064
120	Ham	Boiled (purchased cooked and sliced)	As purchased, lean and fat	100	48·6	2·72	0·045
121	Ham or Pork, chopped	Tinned, as purchased	Six varieties	100	53·6	2·43	—
122	Hare	Roast (with basting)	Flesh only	38	59·0	5·18	0·099
122*a*	Hare (weighed with bone)	Roast (with basting)	Flesh only	38	40·1	3·52	0·067
123	Hare	Stewed	Flesh only	44	60·7	4·78	0·060
123*a*	Hare (weighed with bone)	Stewed	Flesh only	44	44·3	3·48	0·044
124	Heart, sheep	Roast	Ventricles only	53	57·3	4·18	0·174
125	Kidney, ox	Raw	All	—	75·5	2·82	0·094
126	Kidney, ox	Stewed	All	54	66·0	4·24	0·147
127	Kidney, sheep	Raw	Pelvis and capsule removed	—	77·4	2·86	0·103
128	Kidney, sheep	Fried	Pelvis and capsule removed	53	59·3	4·71	0·137
129	Lard	Analysed as purchased	All	100	1·0	Tr.	0·0
130	Liver, mixed sample	Raw	All	—	73·3	2·73	0·081
131	Liver, calf	Sliced and fried after rolling in flour	All	64	50·8	4·78	0·143
132	Liver, ox	Sliced and fried after rolling in flour	All	67	47·7	4·84	0·143
133	Meat paste	Analysed as purchased	Chicken and ham, 3 varieties; ham and tongue, 2 varieties	100	60·5	3·15	—

Meat, Poultry and Game—*continued*

No.	Food.	g. per 100 g.			Calories per 100 g.	mg. per 100 g.									Acid-base balance c.c. per 100 g.	
		Protein.	Fat.	Carbohydrate (as glucose).		Na.	K.	Ca.	Mg.	Fe.	Cu.	P.	S.	Cl.	$\frac{N}{10}$ Acid.	$\frac{N}{10}$ Alkali.
117	Guinea-fowl, roast ..	32·5	8·2	0·0	210	136	430	19·2	28·7	9·3	—	292	363	179	263	
117*a*	Guinea-fowl, roast (weighed with bone)	17·2	4·3	0·0	112	72	228	10·2	15·2	4·9	—	155	192	95	139	
118	Ham, York, raw ..	15·0	49·0	0·0	517	(1120)	345	14·2	15·6	1·2	—	104	174	(1770)	76	
119	Ham, boiled, lean only..	23·1	13·4	0·0	219	(2100)	454	17·0	23·5	2·6	—	244	280	(3350)	223	
120	Ham, boiled, lean and fat	16·3	39·6	0·0	435	(1490)	322	12·7	17·4	2·5	—	192	198	(2350)	162	
121	Ham or Pork, chopped..	15·2	29·9	Tr.	340	(1540)	223	11·8	16·6	1·5	0·09	136	—	(2120)	—	—
122	Hare, roast	31·2	7·0	0·0	193	53	403	28·2	30·0	9·8	0·24	337	347	108	300	
122*a*	Hare, roast (weighed with bone)	21·3	4·8	0·0	131	36	274	19·2	20·4	6·7	0·16	229	236	74	204	
123	Hare, stewed	29·2	8·0	0·0	194	40	211	20·7	22·2	10·8	—	248	320	74	281	
123*a*	Hare, stewed (weighed with bone)	21·3	5·8	0·0	142	29	154	15·1	16·2	7·9	—	181	234	54	205	
124	Heart, sheep, roast ..	25·0	14·7	0·0	239	153	370	9·5	34·9	8·1	—	389	296	125	276	
125	Kidney, ox, raw ..	17·0	5·3	0·0	119	245	231	14·2	18·3	15·0	—	262	161	256	153	
126	Kidney, ox, stewed ..	25·7	5·8	0·0	159	164	164	20·8	22·4	7·1	—	392	242	144	303	
127	Kidney, sheep, raw ..	16·8	3·1	0·0	98	250	254	13·3	15·8	11·7	0·31	254	166	295	157	
128	Kidney, sheep, fried ..	28·0	9·1	0·0	199	261	304	16·6	26·7	14·5	0·30	433	274	288	310	
129	Lard	Tr.	99·0	0·0	921	2	1	0·8	1·3	0·1	0·02	3	25	4	16	
130	Liver, raw	16·5	8·1	0·0	143	86	325	8·4	20·8	13·9	5·80	313	239	100	236	
131	Liver, calf, fried ..	29·0	14·5	2·4	262	122	407	8·8	23·8	21·7	—	576	431	120	495	
132	Liver, ox, fried	29·5	15·9	4·0	284	92	386	8·6	26·5	20·7	—	550	410	82	469	
133	Meat paste	19·7	12·7	4·2	215	(940)	206	26·5	21·7	3·7	0·09	132	131	(1500)	96	

Meat, Poultry and Game—*continued*

No.	Food.	Method of cooking.	Nature of edible (analysed) material.	Edible matter, as eaten, expressed as a percentage of the weight as purchased.	g. per 100 g.		
					Water.	*Total nitrogen.*	*Purine nitrogen.*
134	Mutton chop	Raw..	Lean only	37	67·1	3·18	0·081
134*a*	Mutton chop (weighed with fat and bone)	Raw..	Lean only	37	24·9	1·18	0·030
135	Mutton chop	Raw..	Lean and fat	77	32·3	2·28	0·049
135*a*	Mutton chop (weighed with bone)	Raw..	Lean and fat	77	24·8	1·76	0·038
136	Mutton chop	Grilled	Lean only	34	53·7	4·38	0·061
136*a*	Mutton chop (weighed with fat and bone)	Grilled	Lean only	34	25·2	2·06	0·029
137	Mutton chop	Grilled	Lean and fat	55	33·6	3·26	0·046
137*a*	Mutton chop (weighed with bone)	Grilled	Lean and fat	55	25·4	2·46	0·035
138	Mutton chop	Covered with egg and breadcrumbs and fried	Lean only	36	44·2	3·82	0·063
138*a*	Mutton chop (weighed with fat and bone)	Covered with egg and breadcrumbs and fried	Lean only	36	16·6	1·43	0·024
139	Mutton chop	Covered with egg and breadcrumbs and fried	Lean and fat	78	20·6	2·54	0·040
139*a*	Mutton chop (weighed with bone)	Covered with egg and breadcrumbs and fried	Lean and fat	78	16·8	2·07	0·033

Meat, Poultry and Game—*continued*

No.	Food.	*g. per 100 g.* Protein.	Fat.	Carbohydrate (as glucose).	Calories per 100 g.	*mg. per 100 g.* Na.	K.	Ca.	Mg.	Fe.	Cu.	P.	S.	Cl.	*Acid-base balance, c.c. per 100 g.* $\frac{N}{10}$ Acid.	$\frac{N}{10}$ Alkali.
134	Mutton chop, raw, lean only	18·8	11·8	0·0	187	91	350	12·6	27·2	1·7	0·16	195	208	84	121	
134*a*	Mutton chop, raw, lean only (weighed with fat and bone)	7·0	4·4	0·0	69	34	130	4·7	10·1	0·6	0·06	72	77	31	45	
135	Mutton chop, raw, lean and fat	13·7	52·5	0·0	544	75	246	12·6	18·7	1·0	0·16	173	149	70	107	
135*a*	Mutton chop, raw, lean and fat (weighed with bone)	10·6	40·5	0·0	419	58	190	9·7	14·4	0·8	0·12	133	115	54	83	
136	Mutton chop, grilled, lean only	26·5	17·5	0·0	271	127	400	20·9	30·0	2·5	0·18	239	286	110	170	
136*a*	Mutton chop, grilled, lean only (weighed with fat and bone)	12·4	8·2	0·0	127	60	188	9·8	14·1	1·2	0·09	112	134	52	80	
137	Mutton chop, grilled, lean and fat	19·9	45·0	0·0	500	102	305	17·8	22·8	2·4	0·18	206	213	90	141	
137*a*	Mutton chop, grilled, lean and fat (weighed with bone)	15·0	34·0	0·0	378	77	230	13·5	17·3	1·8	0·14	156	161	68	107	
138	Mutton chop, fried, lean only	22·8	25·2	5·7	341	116	349	15·4	26·1	3·1	0·13	222	250	134	166	
138*a*	Mutton chop, fried, lean only (weighed with fat and bone)	8·6	9·4	2·1	127	44	131	5·8	9·8	1·2	0·05	83	94	50	62	
139	Mutton chop, fried, lean and fat	15·4	60·1	2·6	629	86	241	14·0	17·9	2·6	0·12	184	166	92	126	
139*a*	Mutton chop, fried, lean and fat (weighed with bone)	12·6	49·0	2·1	512	70	196	11·4	14·6	2·1	0·10	150	135	75	103	

Meat, Poultry and Game—*continued*

No.	Food.	Method of cooking.	Nature of edible (analysed) material.	Edible matter, as eaten, expressed as a percentage of the weight as purchased.	g. per 100 g.		
					Water.	Total nitrogen.	Purine nitrogen.
140	Mutton, leg	Boiled	All except bone	63	45·5	4·29	0·091
141	Mutton, leg	Roast	All except bone	48	52·4	4·15	0·077
142	Mutton, scrag and neck	Stewed	All except bone	46	49·7	3·96	0·056
142*a*	Mutton, scrag and neck weighed with bone)	Stewed	All except bone	46	37·3	2·97	0·042
143	Partridge	Roast with basting)	Flesh only	39	54·5	5·87	0·145
143*a*	Partridge (weighed with bone)	Roast (with basting)	Flesh only	39	32·7	3·52	0·087
144	Pheasant	Roast (with basting)	Flesh only	45	56·9	5·15	0·095
144*a*	Pheasant (weighed with bone)	Roast (with basting)	Flesh only	45	35·8	3·24	0·060
145	Pigeon	Boiled	Flesh only	36	62·1	3·57	0·083
145*a*	Pigeon (weighed with bone)	Boiled	Flesh only	36	27·4	1·57	0·036
146	Pigeon	Roast (with basting)	Flesh only	28	57·2	4·44	0·096
146*a*	Pigeon (weighed with bone)	Roast (with basting)	Flesh only	28	25·2	1·95	0·043
147	Pork, leg	Roast	All except bone	42	49·7	4·07	0·066
148	Pork, loin	Roast	Lean only	39	54·2	3·92	0·064
149	Pork, loin	Roast	Lean and fat	62	38·6	3·21	0·051
150	Pork, loin	Salt smoked (purchased cooked)	Lean only	100	54·0	3·90	0·050
151	Pork, loin chops	Grilled	Lean only	31	48·9	4·20	0·068
151*a*	Pork, loin chops (weighed with bone)	Grilled	Lean only	31	20·0	1·72	0·028

Meat, Poultry and Game—*continued*

No.	Food.	g. per 100 g. Protein.	Fat.	Carbohydrate (as glucose).	Calories per 100 g.	mg. per 100 g. Na.	K.	Ca.	Mg.	Fe.	Cu.	P.	S.	Cl.	Acid-base balance, c.c. per 100 g. N/10 Acid.	N/10 Alkali.
140	Mutton, leg, boiled ..	25·8	16·6	0·0	260	64	273	3·6	27·3	5·1	0·24	238	280	67	225	
141	Mutton, leg, roast ..	25·0	20·4	0·0	292	71	346	4·3	26·4	4·3	—	242	271	62	199	
142	Mutton, scrag and neck, stewed	24·2	24·4	0·0	326	66	186	50·0	26·6	6·8	—	220	259	82	203	
142a	Mutton, scrag and neck, stewed (weighed with bones)	18·2	18·3	0·0	245	50	140	37·5	20·0	5·1	—	165	194	61	152	
143	Partridge, roast	35·2	7·2	0·0	211	100	407	45·8	36·0	7·7	—	313	399	99	279	
143a	Partridge, roast (weighed with bone)	21·1	4·3	0·0	127	60	244	27·5	21·6	4·6	—	188	239	59	167	
144	Pheasant, roast	30·8	9·3	0·0	213	104	411	49·3	35·0	8·4	—	308	306	108	216	
144a	Pheasant, roast (weighed with bone)	19·4	5·9	0·0	134	66	259	31·0	22·1	5·3	—	194	193	68	136	
145	Pigeon, boiled	21·7	13·9	0·0	218	74	299	17·6	31·2	9·8	—	352	243	75	257	
145a	Pigeon, boiled (weighed with bone)	9·6	6·1	0·0	96	33	131	7·8	13·7	4·3	—	155	107	33	113	
146	Pigeon, roast	26·8	13·2	0·0	233	105	410	16·3	33·8	19·4	—	404	302	99	291	
146a	Pigeon, roast (weighed with bone)	11·8	5·8	0·0	102	46	180	7·2	14·9	8·5	—	178	133	44	128	
147	Pork, leg, roast	24·6	23·2	0·0	317	66	308	5·2	22·6	1·7	—	363	253	83	286	
148	Pork, loin, roast, lean only	23·6	20·1	0·0	284	69	353	7·4	23·6	2·6	0·09	206	243	101	170	
149	Pork, loin, roast, lean and fat	19·5	40·4	0·0	455	60	287	7·5	18·0	2·3	0·09	185	199	77	146	
150	Pork, loin, salt, smoked, lean only	23·7	15·7	0·0	243	(1800)	300	27·3	24·1	2·3	—	219	242	(3100)	274	
151	Pork chops, grilled, lean only	25·3	23·7	0·0	325	76	347	9·2	20·7	2·9	0·09	211	261	113	187	
151a	Pork chops, grilled, lean only (weighed with bone)	10·4	9·7	0·0	133	31	142	3·8	8·5	1·2	0·04	86	107	46	77	

Meat, Poultry and Game—*continued*

No.	Food.	Method of cooking.	Nature of edible (analysed) material.	Edible matter, as eaten, expressed as a percentage of the weight as purchased.	g. per 100 g.		
					Water.	Total nitrogen.	Purine nitrogen.
152	Pork, loin chops	Grilled	Lean and fat	60	29·6	3·06	0·049
152*a*	Pork, loin chops (weighed with bone)	Grilled	Lean and fat	60	24·6	2·54	0·041
153	Rabbit	Stewed	Flesh only	35	63·9	4·37	0·061
153*a*	Rabbit (weighed with bone)	Stewed	Flesh only	35	32·5	2·23	0·031
154	Sausage, beef	Fried	All	82	49·2	2·20	—
155	Sausage, pork	Raw	All	—	50·7	1·41	—
156	Sausage, pork	Fried	All	88	48·5	1·83	—
157	Sausage (1943)	Raw	7 samples, mixed beef and pork	—	54·0	1·70	—
158	Sausage (1943)	Grilled	7 samples, mixed beef and pork	75	39·2	2·30	—
159	Sausage, black	Analysed as purchased	All except skin	—	55·8	0·85	0·002
160	Sausage, breakfast	Analysed as purchased	All	100	52·2	1·40	—
161	Suet	Analysed as purchased	All except skin	100	Tr.	0·15	—
162	Sweetbreads	Stewed	All	59	65·6	3·70	0·426
163	Tongue, ox	Pickled in NaCl and sugar and boiled	Muscular portion only, fat at base of tongue and skin discarded	38	48·6	3·12	0·048
164	Tongue, sheep's	Stewed	Muscular portion only, fat at base of tongue and skin discarded	33	56·9	2·91	0·052
165	Tripe, dressed	Stewed (treated with lime before purchase)	All	54	77·6	3·00	0·022
166	Turkey	Roast (with basting)	Flesh only	46	59·0	5·07	0·079
166*a*	Turkey (weighed with bone)	Roast (with basting)	Flesh only	46	35·4	3·04	0·049
167	Veal, fillet	Raw	All	—	74·9	3·37	0·080
168	Veal, frozen (Uruguay and N.Z.)	Raw	All	—	75·2	3·19	0·050
169	Veal cutlet	Covered with egg and breadcrumbs and fried	All	74	54·6	5·02	0·106
170	Veal, fillet	Roast	All	75	55·1	5·06	0·089
171	Venison, haunch	Roast	Flesh only	58	56·8	5·60	0·097

Meat, Poultry and Game—*continued*

No.	Food.	g. per 100 g.			Calories per 100 g.	mg. per 100 g.									Acid-base balance, c.c. per 100 g.	
		Protein.	Fat.	Carbohydrate (as glucose).		Na.	K.	Ca.	Mg.	Fe.	Cu.	P.	S.	Cl.	$\frac{N}{10}$ Acid.	$\frac{N}{10}$ Alkali.
152	Pork chops, grilled, lean and fat	18·6	50·3	0·0	544	59	258	8·3	14·9	2·4	0·09	178	190	72	142	
152*a*	Pork chops, grilled, lean and fat (weighed with bone)	15·4	41·9	0·0	451	49	214	6·9	12·4	2·0	0·07	148	158	60	118	
153	Rabbit, stewed	26·6	7·7	0·0	180	32	210	11·3	21·6	1·9	0·20	199	245	43	201	
153*a*	Rabbit, stewed (weighed with bone)	13·6	3·9	0·0	92	16	107	5·8	11·0	1·0	0·10	102	125	22	102	
154	Sausage, beef, fried ..	13·8	18·4	15·7	287	(1130)	255	21·2	16·6	4·1	0·17	168	163	(1770)	129	
155	Sausage, pork, raw ..	8·8	28·8	9·8	341	(770)	158	15·1	11·5	2·5	0·12	108	73	(1070)	25	
156	Sausage, pork, fried ..	11·5	24·8	12·7	326	(999)	205	19·7	14·9	3·3	0·15	141	95	(1390)	36	
157	Sausage (1943), raw ..	10·6	16·1	14·3	247	(720)	257	(62)	44·0	2·4	0·30	194	—	(975)	—	—
158	Sausage (1943), grilled ..	14·4	20·0	19·4	318	(980)	348	(84)	60·0	3·2	0·40	263	—	(1320)	—	—
159	Sausage, black	5·3	22·5	14·7	286	(900)	130	31·2	15·0	19·5	0·26	27	173	(1320)	44	
160	Sausage, breakfast ..	8·7	20·4	16·8	288	(880)	170	21·9	16·4	1·9	0·08	86	79	(1300)	20	
161	Suet	0·9	99·0	0·0	924	21	13	6·0	1·1	0·4	0·04	7	20	18	6	
162	Sweetbreads, stewed ..	22·7	9·1	0·0	178	69	231	14·3	15·4	1·6	—	596	185	74	117	
163	Tongue, ox, pickled ..	19·1	23·9	2·3	309	(1870)	152	30·9	16·2	3·0	—	229	200	(3000)	236	
164	Tongue, sheep's, stewed	18·0	24·0	0·0	297	79	109	11·1	13·2	3·4	—	196	187	80	187	
165	Tripe, stewed	18·0	3·0	0·0	102	72	9	(127)	7·9	1·6	—	132	145	30	81	
166	Turkey, roast	30·2	7·7	0·0	196	130	367	38·3	28·2	3·8	—	320	234	123	195	
166*a*	Turkey, roast (weighed with bone)	18·1	4·6	0·0	118	78	220	23·0	16·9	2·3	—	192	140	74	117	
167	Veal, fillet, raw	20·1	2·7	0·0	108	107	357	7·6	25·0	2·3	—	258	220	68	161	
168	Veal, frozen, raw ..	18·7	3·6	0·0	110	95	370	10·2	25·0	1·8	0·15	200	208	98	124	
169	Veal cutlet, fried ..	30·4	8·1	4·4	216	106	422	10·0	32·7	2·6	—	283	329	115	235	
170	Veal, fillet, roast ..	30·5	11·5	0·0	232	97	427	14·3	27·6	2·5	—	355	330	113	285	
171	Venison, roast	33·5	6·4	0·0	197	86	364	29·0	33·4	7·8	—	286	321	89	238	

Fish

No.	Food.	Nature of raw material.	Method of cooking.	Nature of edible (analysed) material.	Edible matter, as eaten, expressed as a percentage of the weight as purchased.	g. per 100 g.		
						Water.	Total nitrogen.	Purine nitrogen.
172	Bass..	Whole fish, excluding guts	Steamed	Flesh and skin ..	47	73·3	3·26	0·073
172*a*	Bass (weighed with bones)	Whole fish, excluding guts	Steamed	Flesh and skin ..	47	38·9	1·73	0·039
173	Bloaters	Body of fish without heads, roes or guts	Grilled	Flesh only	65	55·6	3·76	0·133
173*a*	Bloaters (weighed with bones and skin)	Body of fish without heads, roes or guts	Grilled	Flesh only	65	41·1	2·78	0·098
174	Bream, Red	Whole fish, excluding guts	Steamed	Flesh and skin ..	47	73·5	3·39	0·069
174*a*	Bream, Red (weighed with bones)	Whole fish, excluding guts	Steamed	Flesh and skin ..	47	38·2	1·76	0·036
175	Bream, Sea	Whole fish, excluding guts	Steamed	Flesh and skin ..	58	76·5	3·07	0·072
175*a*	Bream, Sea (weighed with bones	Whole fish, excluding guts	Steamed	Flesh and skin ..	58	49·7	2·00	0·047
176	Brill	Pieces from tail end	Steamed	Flesh only	63	74·2	3·39	0·061
176*a*	Brill (weighed with bones and skin)	Pieces from tail end	Steamed	Flesh only	63	50·5	2·30	0·042
177	Catfish	Middle cuts, skinned	Steamed	All except bones ..	64	73·6	3·43	0·060
177*a*	Catfish (weighed with bones)	Middle cuts, skinned	Steamed	All except bones ..	64	62·5	2·92	0·051
178	Catfish	Middle cuts, skinned	Covered with batter and crumbs and fried	All except bones ..	90	61·9	3·17	0·065
178*a*	Catfish (weighed with bones)	Middle cuts, skinned	Covered with batter and crumbs and fried	All except bones ..	90	58·0	2·98	0·061

Fish—*continued*

No.	Food.	g. per 100 g.			Calories per 100 g.	mg. per 100 g.									Acid-base balance, c.c. per 100 g.	
		Protein.	Fat.	Carbohydrate (as glucose).		Na.	K.	Ca.	Mg.	Fe.	Cu.	P.	S.	Cl.	$\frac{N}{10}$ Acid.	$\frac{N}{10}$ Alkali.
172	Bass, steamed	19·5	5·1	0·0	127	75	326	46·9	26·9	0·7	—	220	233	85	150	
172*a*	Bass, steamed (weighed with bones)	10·4	2·7	0·0	67	40	173	24·9	14·2	0·4	—	117	124	45	79	
173	Bloaters, grilled	22·6	17·4	0·0	255	(703)	446	123·0	44·7	2·2	—	355	308	(1130)	741	
173*a*	Bloaters, grilled (weighed with bones and skin)	16·7	12·9	0·0	189	(520)	330	91·0	33·1	1·6	—	263	228	(838)	550	
174	Bream, Red, steamed ..	19·7	4·0	0·0	118	119	345	27·9	29·9	0·4	—	213	242	138	148	
174*a*	Bream, Red, steamed (weighed with bones)	10·2	2·1	0·0	61	62	179	14·5	15·6	0·2	—	111	126	72	77	
175	Bream, Sea, steamed ..	17·8	3·0	0·0	101	113	281	35·0	26·7	0·6	—	238	219	122	164	
175*a*	Bream, Sea, steamed (weighed with bones)	11·6	2·0	0·0	66	73	182	22·7	17·4	0·4	—	155	142	79	106	
176	Brill, steamed	20·4	3·4	0·0	115	94	264	15·3	31·0	0·7	0·13	230	214	125	175	
176*a*	Brill, steamed (weighed with bones and skin)	13·9	2·3	0·0	78	64	180	10·4	21·1	0·5	0·09	157	146	85	119	
177	Catfish, steamed ..	20·4	3·7	0·0	118	108	317	13·9	26·6	0·6	—	212	215	108	145	
177*a*	Catfish, steamed (weighed with bones)	17·4	3·2	0·0	100	92	269	11·8	22·6	0·5	—	180	183	92	123	
178	Catfish, fried	18·8	10·5	6·5	200	120	323	19·1	25·7	2·3	—	228	199	150	148	
178*a*	Catfish, fried (weighed with bones)	17·7	9·9	6·1	188	113	304	18·0	24·2	2·2	—	215	187	141	139	

Fish—*continued*

No.	Food.	Nature of raw material.	Method of cooking.	Nature of edible (analysed) material.	Edible matter, as eaten, expressed as a percentage of the weight as purchased.	g. per 100 g. Water.	Total nitrogen.	Purine nitrogen.
179	Cockles	Purchased cooked without shells	.. .. ..	All	100	78·9	1·80	0·051
180	Cod	Middle cuts ..	Steamed	Flesh only	66	79·2	2·98	0·062
180*a*	Cod (weighed with bones and skin)	Middle cuts ..	Steamed	Flesh only	66	64·1	2·42	0·050
181	Cod	Steaks	Covered with batter and crumbs and fried	All except bones ..	114	69·4	3·44	0·063
181*a*	Cod (weighed with bones) ..	Steaks	Covered with batter and crumbs and fried	All except bones ..	114	63·1	3·13	0·057
182	Cod	Steaks	Grilled with added butter	Flesh only	54	64·6	4·56	0·082
182*a*	Cod (weighed with bones and skin)	Steaks	Grilled with added butter	Flesh only	54	54·9	3·87	0·070
183	Cod roe	Half a roe	Parboiled, sliced and fried in crumbs	All	93	62·0	3·35	0·112
184	Cod roe	Half a roe	Baked in vinegar ..	All	98	71·1	3·85	0·130
185	Conger	Cut from behind head	Steamed	Flesh only	60	73·3	3·77	0·063
185*a*	Conger (weighed with bones and skin)	Cut from behind head	Steamed	Flesh only	60	55·0	2·83	0·047
186	Conger	Steaks from behind head	Covered with batter and crumbs and fried	All except bones ..	91	52·7	3·10	0·070
186*a*	Conger (weighed with bones)	Steaks from behind head	Covered with batter and crumbs and fried	All except bones ..	91	46·3	2·73	0·062

Fish—*continued*

No.	Food.	g. per 100 g. Protein.	Fat.	Carbohydrate (as glucose).	Calories per 100 g.	mg. per 100 g. Na.	K.	Ca.	Mg.	Fe.	Cu.	P.	S.	Cl.	Acid-base balance, c.c. per 100 g. $\frac{N}{10}$ Acid.	$\frac{N}{10}$ Alkali.
179	Cockles	11·0	0·3	Tr.	48	(3520)	43	127·0	51·0	26·0	—	204	322	(5220)	156	
180	Cod, steamed	18·0	0·9	0·0	82	100	360	14·6	20·6	0·5	0·10	242	212	120	162	
180a	Cod, steamed (weighed with bones and skin)	14·6	0·7	0·0	66	81	292	11·8	16·7	0·4	0·08	196	172	97	131	
181	Cod, fried	20·7	4·7	2·9	140	161	342	49·6	26·8	1·0	0·10	261	243	145	156	
181a	Cod, fried (weighed with bones)	18·8	4·3	2·6	127	146	311	45·2	24·4	0·9	0·09	238	221	132	142	
182	Cod, grilled	27·0	5·3	0·0	160	110	407	31·0	36·0	1·0	—	274	323	130	218	
182a	Cod, grilled (weighed with bones and skin)	22·9	4·5	0·0	136	94	346	26·4	30·6	0·9	—	233	274	111	185	
183	Cod roe, fried	20·6	11·9	3·0	206	127	258	16·8	10·5	1·6	—	504	238	188	388	
184	Cod roe, baked in vinegar	24·0	3·2	0·0	128	73	132	13·0	8·0	2·3	—	402	272	173	400	
185	Conger steamed ..	22·8	1·8	0·0	110	99	347	29·8	28·4	0·5	—	220	269	82	163	
185a	Conger, steamed (weighed with bones and skin)	17·1	1·4	0·0	83	74	260	22·4	21·3	0·4	—	165	202	62	122	
186	Conger, fried	18·7	20·0	6·5	287	108	353	24·2	29·4	1·0	—	247	222	156	168	
186a	Conger, fried (weighed with bones)	16·4	17·6	5·7	252	95	310	21·3	25·8	0·9	—	217	195	137	148	

Fish—*continued*

No.	Food.	Nature of raw material.	Method of cooking.	Nature of edible (analysed) material.	Edible matter, as eaten, expressed as a percentage of the weight as purchased.	g. per 100 g.		
						Water.	Total nitrogen.	Purine nitrogen.
187	Crab	Alive	Boiled in fresh water	Flesh only	16	72·5	3·21	0·061
187*a*	Crab (weighed with shell)..	Alive	Boiled in fresh water	Flesh only	16	14·5	0·64	0·012
188	Dabs	Whole fish, excluding guts	Covered with batter and crumbs and fried	All except bones ..	91	19·9	3·19	0·065
188*a*	Dabs (weighed with bones)	Whole fish, excluding guts	Covered with batter and crumbs and fried	All except bones ..	91	15·9	2·55	0·052
189	Dogfish	Tail ends, skinned ..	Covered with batter and crumbs and fried	All except bones ..	90	44·4	3·66	0·050
189*a*	Dogfish (weighed with bone)	Tail ends, skinned ..	Covered with batter and crumbs and fried	All except bones ..	90	40·3	3·33	0·045
190	Eels, elvers	Whole fish	Raw..	All	100	81·8	2·02	—
191	Eels, silver	Live eels	Raw..	Flesh only	66	57·1	2·31	—
191*a*	Eels, silver (weighed with bones and skin)	Live eels	Raw..	Flesh only	66	37·8	1·52	—
192	Eels, silver	Live eels	Stewed in half their weight of water	Flesh only	50	49·2	2·84	—
193	Eels, yellow	Live eels	Raw..	Flesh only	67	71·3	2·66	—
193*a*	Eels, yellow (weighed with bones and skin)	Live eels	Raw..	Flesh only	67	47·8	1·78	—
194	Fillet, smoked	Fillet as purchased	Steamed	All	67	75·2	3·25	0·048
195	Fish paste	Analysed as purchased	.. .. ..	Salmon and shrimp, 3 varieties; salmon and anchovy, 2 varieties; bloater, 3 varieties	100	64·5	2·38	—

Fish—*continued*

No.	Food.	*g. per 100 g.*			Calories per 100 g.	*mg. per 100 g.*									*Acid-base balance, c.c. per 100 g.*	
		Protein.	*Fat.*	*Carbohydrate (as glucose).*		*Na.*	*K.*	*Ca.*	*Mg.*	*Fe.*	*Cu.*	*P.*	*S.*	*Cl.*	$\frac{N}{10}$ *Acid.*	$\frac{N}{10}$ *Alkali.*
187	Crab, boiled	19·2	5·2	0·0	127	366	271	29·4	47·9	1·3	—	350	465	570	395	
187*a*	Crab, boiled (weighed with shell)	3·8	1·0	0·0	25	73	54	5·9	9·6	0·3	—	70	93	114	79	
188	Dabs, fried	19·2	14·3	9·8	249	127	284	130·0	29·1	1·0	0·07	250	259	245	175	
188*a*	Dabs, fried (weighed with bones)	15·4	11·4	7·8	199	102	227	104·0	23·3	0·8	0·06	200	207	196	140	
189	Dogfish, fried	17·9	25·2	6·0	330	163	245	12·5	20·0	1·3	—	269	210	203	205	
189*a*	Dogfish, fried weighed with bone)	16·3	22·9	5·5	300	148	223	11·4	18·2	1·2	—	244	191	184	186	
190	Eels, elvers, raw ..	12·6	2·2	0·0	72	67	230	515·0	31·0	4·0	Tr.	440	141	55	16	
191	Eels, silver, raw.. ..	14·4	27·8	0·0	318	77	215	12·6	14·3	0·8	0·03	192	162	69	138	
191*a*	Eels, silver, raw (weighed with bones and skin)	9·5	18·4	0·0	211	51	142	8·3	9·4	0·5	0·02	127	107	46	91	
192	Eels, silver, stewed ..	17·7	32·4	0·0	374	73	200	14·4	14·8	1·0	—	200	199	64	168	
193	Eels, yellow, raw ..	16·6	11·3	0·0	173	89	267	18·5	19·0	0·7	0·05	223	187	57	145	
193*a*	Eels, yellow, raw (weighed with bones and skin)	11·1	7·4	0·0	115	60	179	12·4	12·7	0·5	0·03	150	125	38	96	
194	Fillet, smoked, steamed	19·4	0·9	0·0	88	(1080)	268	19·6	43·9	1·0	—	222	248	(1550)	149	
195	Fish paste	14·9	9·5	6·5	174	(1480)	307	146·0	30·1	6·0	0·06	210	185	(2380)	103	

Fish—*continued*

No.	Food.	Nature of raw material.	Method of cooking.	Nature of edible (analysed) material.	Edible matter, as eaten, expressed as a percentage of the weight as purchased.	g. per 100 g.		
						Water.	Total. nitrogen.	Purine nitrogen.
196	Flounder	Body of fish without head or guts	Steamed	Flesh only	45	76·6	3·24	0·086
196*a*	Flounder (weighed with bones and skin)	Body of fish without head or guts	Steamed	Flesh only	45	42·8	1·81	0·048
197	Flounder	Body of fish without head or guts	Covered with batter and crumbs and fried	Flesh and skin ..	74	61·5	2·84	0·061
197*a*	Flounder (weighed with bones)	Body of fish without head or guts	Covered with batter and crumbs and fried	Flesh and skin ..	74	42·4	1·96	0·042
198	Gurnet, grey	Body of fish without head or guts	Steamed	Flesh only	61	72·0	3·46	0·085
198*a*	Gurnet, grey (weighed with bones and skin)	Body of fish without head or guts	Steamed	Flesh only	61	58·2	2·80	0·069
199	Gurnet, red	Body of fish without head or guts	Steamed	Flesh only	57	71·6	3·54	0·079
199*a*	Gurnet, red (weighed with bones and skin)	Body of fish without head or guts	Steamed	Flesh only	57	50·9	2·51	0·056
200	Haddock, fresh	Fillets	Raw..	Flesh only	—	81·3	2·68	0·067
201	Haddock, fresh	Middle cut	Steamed	Flesh only	59	75·1	3·65	0·072
201*a*	Haddock, fresh (weighed with bones and skin)	Middle cut	Steamed	Flesh only	59	57·1	2·77	0·055
202	Haddock, fresh	Body of fish without head or guts	Covered with batter and crumbs and fried	All except bones ..	115	65·1	3·42	0·083
202*a*	Haddock, fresh (weighed with bones)	Body of fish without head or guts	Covered with batter and crumbs and fried	All except bones ..	115	60·0	3·15	0·076

Fish—*continued*

No.	Food.	g. per 100 g.			Calories per 100 g.	mg. per 100 g.									Acid-base balance, c.c. per 100 g.	
		Protein.	Fat.	Carbohydrate (as glucose).		Na.	K.	Ca.	Mg.	Fe.	Cu.	P.	S.	Cl.	$\frac{N}{10}$ Acid.	$\frac{N}{10}$ Alkali.
196	Flounder, steamed ..	19·4	1·7	0·0	95	115	318	55·1	25·0	1·3	—	296	231	148	197	
196*a*	Flounder, steamed (weighed with bones and skin)	10·9	1·0	0·0	53	64	178	30·9	14·0	0·7	—	166	129	83	110	
197	Flounder, fried	17·0	12·9	6·5	214	130	282	74·5	22·6	1·1	—	218	203	200	139	
197*a*	Flounder, fried (weighed with bones)	11·7	8·9	4·5	147	90	194	51·3	15·6	0·8	—	150	140	138	96	
198	Gurnet, grey, steamed ..	21·0	5·2	0·0	134	117	305	13·1	23·9	0·8	—	196	247	117	158	
198*a*	Gurnet, grey, steamed (weighed with bones and skin)	17·0	4·2	0·0	108	95	247	10·6	19·4	0·6	—	158	200	95	128	
199	Gurnet, red, steamed ..	21·3	4·7	0·0	131	186	350	20·9	30·9	0·7	—	241	253	141	146	
199*a*	Gurnet, red, steamed (weighed with bones and skin)	15·1	3·3	0·0	93	132	248	14·8	21·9	0·5	—	171	180	100	104	
200	Haddock, fillets, raw ..	15·9	0·6	0·0	71	125	302	31·7	22·5	1·0	—	216	223	156	156	
201	Haddock, fresh, steamed	22·0	0·8	0·0	97	121	323	54·6	27·8	0·7	0·13	234	304	78	177	
201*a*	Haddock, fresh, steamed (weighed with bones and skin)	16·7	0·6	0·0	74	92	245	41·4	21·2	0·5	0·10	178	231	59	134	
202	Haddock, fresh, fried ..	20·4	8·3	3·6	175	177	348	114·0	30·6	1·2	—	247	285	181	140	
202*a*	Haddock, fresh, fried (weighed with bones)	18·8	7·6	3·3	161	163	320	105·0	28·2	1·1	—	227	262	166	129	

Fish—*continued*

No.	Food.	Nature of raw material.	Method of cooking.	Nature of edible (analysed) material.	Edible matter, as eaten, expressed as a percentage of the weight as purchased.	g. per 100 g. Water.	Total nitrogen.	Purine nitrogen.
203	Haddock, smoked ..	As purchased ..	Steamed	Flesh only	55	71·6	3·73	0·065
203*a*	Haddock, smoked (weighed with bones and skin)	As purchased ..	Steamed	Flesh only	55	46·5	2·42	0·042
204	Hake	Middle cut	Steamed	Flesh only	63	76·1	3·11	0·061
204*a*	Hake (weighed with bones and skin)	Middle cut	Steamed	Flesh only	63	61·0	2·49	0·049
205	Hake	Steaks	Covered with batter and crumbs and fried	All except bones ..	106	62·0	3·18	0·052
205*a*	Hake (weighed with bones)	Steaks	Covered with batter and crumbs and fried	All except bones ..	106	58·3	2·99	0·049
206	Halibut	Middle cut	Steamed	Flesh only	66	70·9	3·80	0·068
206*a*	Halibut (weighed with bones and skin)	Middle cut	Steamed	Flesh only	66	53·8	2·88	0·052
207	Herring	Fillets	Raw..	All except bones ..	—	63·5	2·70	0·119
208	Herring	Body of fish without head or guts	Covered with oatmeal and fried	Flesh, skin and roes	77	58·7	3·69	0·172
208*a*	Herring (weighed with bones)	Body of fish without head or guts	Covered with oatmeal and fried	Flesh, skin and roes	77	51·6	3·24	0·151
209	Herring	Body of fish without head or guts	Baked in vinegar ..	Flesh, skin and roes	78	67·5	2·89	0·160
209*a*	Herring (weighed with bones)	Body of fish without head or guts	Baked in vinegar ..	Flesh, skin and roes	78	62·0	2·65	0·147
210	Herring roe (soft)	Whole roes ..	Rolled in flour and fried	All	80	52·3	3·85	0·484

Fish—*continued*

No.	Food.	*g. per 100 g.*			Calories per 100 g.	*mg. per 100 g.*									*Acid-base balance, c.c. per 100 g.*	
		Protein.	*Fat.*	*Carbohydrate (as glucose).*		*Na.*	*K.*	*Ca.*	*Mg.*	*Fe.*	*Cu.*	*P.*	*S.*	*Cl.*	$\frac{N}{10}$ *Acid.*	$\frac{N}{10}$ *Alkali.*
203	Haddock, smoked, steamed	22·3	0·9	0·0	100	(1220)	293	57·5	25·4	1·0	—	248	253	(1900)	197	
203*a*	Haddock, smoked, steamed (weighed with bones and skin)	14·5	0·6	0·0	65	(793)	190	37·4	16·5	0·7	—	162	164	(1230)	128	
204	Hake, steamed	18·5	3·3	0·0	107	118	310	15·9	26·7	0·6	0·12	218	193	95	127	
204*a*	Hake, steamed (weighed with bones and skin)	14·8	2·6	0·0	86	95	248	12·7	21·4	0·5	0·10	175	154	76	102	
205	Hake, fried	19·3	11·4	5·3	205	153	297	25·8	29·0	0·9	0·17	259	197	134	148	
205*a*	Hake, fried (weighed with bones)	18·2	10·7	5·0	193	144	279	24·3	27·3	0·8	0·16	244	185	126	139	
206	Halibut, steamed ..	22·7	4·0	0·0	130	111	340	13·0	23·2	0·6	0·07	255	255	80	186	
206*a*	Halibut, steamed (weighed with bones and skin)	17·3	3·0	0·0	99	84	258	9·9	17·6	0·5	0·05	194	194	61	141	
207	Herring, raw	16·7	18·1	0·0	273	130	317	101·0	31·7	1·5	—	272	191	122	115	
208	Herring, fried	21·8	15·1	1·5	235	101	415	38·6	34·7	1·9	—	339	261	125	219	
208*a*	Herring, fried (weighed with bones)	19·2	13·3	1·3	208	89	365	34·0	30·5	1·7	—	298	230	110	193	
209	Herring, baked in vinegar	16·9	12·9	0·0	189	62	233	58·2	21·8	1·6	—	326	205	119	238	
209*a*	Herring, baked in vinegar (weighed with bones)	15·5	11·8	0·0	174	57	214	53·5	20·1	1·5	—	300	188	109	219	
210	Herring roe, fried ..	23·4	15·8	4·7	260	87	239	15·7	8·1	1·5	—	915	242	123	662	

Fish—*continued*

No.	Food.	Nature of raw material.	Method of cooking.	Nature of edible (analysed) material.	Edible matter, as eaten, expressed as a percentage of the weight as purchased.	g. per 100 g.		
						Water.	Total nitrogen	Purine nitrogen.
211	John Dory	Whole fish without head, guts or fins	Steamed	Flesh only	50	76·7	3·28	0·057
211*a*	John Dory (weighed with bones and skin)	Whole fish without head, guts or fins	Steamed	Flesh only	50	47·5	2·04	0·035
212	Kippers	As purchased ..	Baked	Flesh only	45	58·7	4·08	0·091
212*a*	Kippers (weighed with bones and skin)	As purchased ..	Baked	Flesh only	45	31·6	2·20	0·049
213	Lemon sole	Whole fish without head, guts or fins	Steamed	Flesh only	62	77·2	3·29	0·054
213*a*	Lemon sole (weighed with bones and skin)	Whole fish without head, guts or fins	Steamed	Flesh only	62	54·9	2·34	0·038
214	Lemon sole..	Whole fish without head, guts or fins	Covered with batter and crumbs and fried	All except bones ..	91	60·4	2·57	0·044
214*a*	Lemon sole (weighed with bones)	Whole fish without head, guts or fins	Covered with batter and crumbs and fried	All except bones ..	91	47·7	2·03	0·035
215	Ling..	Sections from body	Steamed	Flesh only	60	74·6	3·73	0·060
215*a*	Ling (weighed with bones and skin)	Sections from body	Steamed	Flesh only	60	55·9	2·79	0·045
216	Ling..	Steaks	Covered with batter and crumbs and fried	All except bones ..	100	62·1	2·85	0·056
216*a*	Ling (weighed with bones)	Steaks	Covered with batter and crumbs and fried	All except bones ..	100	55·2	2·54	0·050

Fish—*continued*

No.	Food.	*g. per 100 g.* Protein.	Fat.	Carbohydrate (as glucose).	Calories per 100 g.	*mg. per 100 g.* Na.	K.	Ca.	Mg.	Fe.	Cu.	P.	S.	Cl.	*Acid-base balance, c.c. per 100 g.* $\frac{N}{10}$ Acid.	$\frac{N}{10}$ Alkali.
211	John Dory, steamed ..	19·9	1·4	0·0	95	139	287	23·0	29·0	0·6	—	251	234	143	179	
211*a*	John Dory, steamed (weighed with bones and skin)	12·3	0·9	0·0	59	86	178	14·3	18·0	0·4	—	156	145	89	111	
212	Kippers, baked	23·2	11·4	0·0	201	(990)	520	64·8	47·5	1·4	—	426	280	(1520)	245	
212*a*	Kippers, baked (weighed with bones and skin)	12·5	6·2	0·0	108	(535)	281	35·0	25·7	0·8	—	230	151	(824)	132	
213	Lemon sole, steamed ..	19·9	0·9	0·0	90	115	279	20·6	20·0	0·6	0·12	247	241	117	194	
213*a*	Lemon sole, steamed (weighed with bones and skin)	14·1	0·6	0·0	64	82	198	14·6	14·2	0·4	0·09	175	171	83	138	
214	Lemon sole, fried ..	15·4	13·0	9·3	219	136	250	95·0	22·3	1·1	0·16	241	189	124	119	
214*a*	Lemonsole, fried (weighed with bones)	12·2	10·3	7·4	173	108	198	75·0	15·8	0·9	0·13	190	149	98	84	
215	Ling, steamed	22·4	0·8	0·0	99	120	370	17·6	36·9	0·5	—	221	266	99	149	
215*a*	Ling, steamed (weighed with bones and skin)	16·8	0·6	0·0	74	90	278	13·2	27·7	0·4	—	166	199	74	112	
216	Ling, fried	16·8	12·4	6·3	208	145	312	39·8	32·0	0·8	—	228	203	157	128	
216*a*	Ling, fried (weighed with bones)	15·0	11·0	5·6	185	129	278	35·4	28·5	0·7	—	203	181	140	114	

Fish—*continued*

No.	Food.	Nature of raw material.	Method of cooking.	Nature of edible (analysed) material.	Edible matter, as eaten, expressed as a percentage of the weight as purchased.	g. per 100 g.		
						Water.	Total nitrogen.	Purine nitrogen.
217	Lobster	Alive	Boiled in fresh water	Flesh only	29	72·4	3·54	0·073
217*a*	Lobster (weighed with shell)	Alive	Boiled in fresh water	Flesh only	29	26·1	1·27	0·026
218	Mackerel	Body of fish without head or guts	Fried	Flesh only	61	65·6	3·44	0·100
218*a*	Mackerel (weighed with bones and skin)	Body of fish without head or guts	Fried	Flesh only	61	47·8	2·51	0·073
219	Megrim	Fillets	Raw..	All except bones ..	—	80·0	2·85	0·046
220	Megrim	Whole fish without guts	Steamed	Flesh only	54	75·9	3·45	0·057
220*a*	Megrim (weighed with bones and skin)	Whole fish without guts	Steamed	Flesh only	54	50·8	2·32	0·038
221	Megrim	Whole fish without head, fins or guts	Covered with batter and crumbs and fried	All except bones ..	92	57·0	3·29	0·065
221*a*	Megrim (weighed with bones)	Whole fish without head, fins or guts	Covered with batter and crumbs and fried	All except bones ..	92	48·5	2·80	0·055
222	Monkfish	Tail ends skinned ..	Steamed	All except bones ..	53	75·4	3·58	0·053
222*a*	Monkfish (weighed with bones)	Tail ends skinned ..	Steamed	All except bones ..	53	61·1	2·90	0·043
223	Monkfish	Tail ends skinned ..	Covered with batter and crumbs and fried	All except bones ..	78	66·3	2·88	0·066
223*a*	Monkfish (weighed with bones)	Tail ends skinned ..	Covered with batter and crumbs and fried	All except bones ..	78	57·0	2·48	0·057

Fish—*continued*

No.	Food.	g. per 100 g. Protein.	Fat.	Carbohydrate (as glucose).	Calories per 100 g.	mg. per 100 g. Na.	K.	Ca.	Mg.	Fe.	Cu.	P.	S.	Cl.	Acid-base balance, c.c. per 100 g. $\frac{N}{10}$ Acid.	$\frac{N}{10}$ Alkali.
217	Lobster, boiled	21·2	3·4	0·0	119	325	258	61·9	34·3	0·8	—	283	514	525	384	
217a	Lobster, boiled (weighed with shell)	7·6	1·2	0·0	43	117	93	22·2	12·3	0·3	—	102	185	189	138	
218	Mackerel, fried	20·0	11·3	0·0	187	153	418	28·4	34·8	1·2	0·20	280	210	114	127	
218a	Mackerel, fried (weighed with bones and skin)	14·6	8·3	0·0	136	112	305	20·7	25·4	0·9	0·15	204	153	83	93	
219	Megrim, raw	17·1	1·0	0·0	79	121	269	61·8	29·4	1·2	—	187	204	122	105	
220	Megrim, steamed ..	20·7	1·3	0·0	97	96	214	76·0	27·7	0·9	—	218	246	119	171	
220a	Megrim, steamed (weighed with bones and skin)	13·9	0·9	0·0	65	64	144	50·9	18·6	0·6	—	146	165	80	115	
221	Megrim, fried	19·5	11·6	9·5	224	177	251	62·8	31·0	0·6	—	219	235	183	141	
221a	Megrim, fried (weighed with bones)	16·6	9·9	8·1	190	150	214	53·4	26·4	0·5	—	186	200	156	120	
222	Monkfish, steamed ..	21·8	0·9	0·0	98	135	356	10·4	29·6	0·5	—	215	256	136	157	
222a	Monkfish, steamed (weighed with bones)	17·7	0·7	0·0	79	109	288	8·4	24·0	0·4	—	174	207	110	127	
223	Monkfish, fried	17·0	8·2	6·1	169	164	400	11·3	31·7	1·2	—	206	206	197	111	
223a	Monkfish, fried (weighed with bones)	14·6	7·1	5·3	145	141	344	9·7	27·2	1·0	—	177	177	169	96	

Fish—*continued*

No.	Food.	Nature of raw material.	Method of cooking.	Nature of edible (analysed) material.	Edible matter, as eaten, expressed as a percentage of the weight as purchased.	g. per 100 g. Water.	Total nitrogen.	Purine nitrogen.
224	Mullet, grey	Whole fish without guts	Steamed	Flesh only	55	72·7	3·52	0·073
224*a*	Mullet, grey (weighed with bones and skin)	Whole fish without guts	Steamed	Flesh only	55	46·5	2·25	0·047
225	Mullet, red	Whole fish without guts	Steamed	Flesh and skin ..	53	71·6	3·62	0·081
225*a*	Mullet, red (weighed with bones)	Whole fish without guts	Steamed	Flesh and skin ..	53	47·3	2·38	0·054
226	Mussels	Alive in shells ..	Raw..	Flesh only	32	84·1	1·93	0·199
227	Mussels	Alive in shells ..	Boiled in fresh water	Flesh only	20	79·0	2·75	0·154
227*a*	Mussels (weighed with shells)	Alive in shells ..	Boiled in fresh water	Flesh only	20	23·7	0·83	0·046
228	Oysters	Alive in shells ..	Raw..	Flesh only	12	85·7	1·72	0·044
228*a*	Oysters (weighed with shell)	Alive in shells ..	Raw..	Flesh only	12	10·3	0·21	0·005
229	Pilchards	Tinned, with added water and salt	.. .. ..	Fish, except backbone	79	65·5	3·50	—
230	Pilchards	Tinned, with added water and salt	.. .. ..	Everything in tin except backbone	97	64·0	3·02	—
231	Plaice	Fillets	Raw..	All except bones ..	—	80·8	2·59	0·065
232	Plaice	Body of fish without head, fins or guts	Steamed	Flesh only	49	78·0	3·02	0·053
232*a*	Plaice (weighed with bones and skin)	Body of fish without head, fins or guts	Steamed	Flesh only	49	42·1	1·63	0·029
233	Plaice	Body of fish without head, fins or guts	Covered with batter and crumbs and fried	All except bones ..	61	58·5	3·02	0·047
233*a*	Plaice (weighed with bones)	Body of fish without head, fins or guts	Covered with batter and crumbs and fried	All except bones ..	61	35·6	1·84	0·029
234	Pollack	Middle cut	Steamed	Flesh only	68	20·7	3·33	0·071
234*a*	Pollack (weighed with bones and skin)	Middle cut	Steamed	Flesh only	68	17·8	2·86	0·061

Fish—*continued*

No.	Food.	g. per 100 g.			Calories per 100 g.	mg. per 100 g.									Acid-base balance, c.c. per 100 g.	
		Protein.	Fat.	Carbohydrate (as glucose).		Na.	K.	Ca.	Mg.	Fe.	Cu.	P.	S.	Cl.	$\frac{N}{10}$ Acid.	$\frac{N}{10}$ Alkali.
224	Mullet, grey. steamed ..	21·6	4·0	0·0	126	94	275	14·2	30·0	2·0	—	256	252	77	201	
224a	Mullet, grey, steamed (weighed with bones and skin)	13·8	2·6	0·0	81	60	176	9·1	19·2	1·3	—	164	161	49	128	
225	Mullet, red, steamed ..	21·4	4·3	0·0	128	118	364	29·2	32·8	0·9	—	282	258	101	185	
225a	Mullet, red, steamed (weighed with bones)	14·1	2·8	0·0	85	78	240	19·3	21·7	0·6	—	186	171	67	122	
226	Mussels, raw	11·7	1·9	Tr.	66	289	315	88·0	22·7	5·8	—	236	367	463	244	
227	Mussels, boiled	16·8	2·0	Tr.	87	210	92	197·0	25·0	13·5	—	331	348	315	287	
227a	Mussels, boiled (weighed with shells)	5·0	0·6	Tr.	26	63	28	59·0	7·5	4·1	—	99	104	95	86	
228	Oysters, raw	10·2	0·9	Tr.	50	505	258	186·0	41·8	6·0	—	267	249	815	144	
228a	Oysters, raw (weighed with shells)	1·2	0·1	Tr.	6	61	31	22·3	5·0	0·7	—	32	30	98	17	
229	Pilchards, tinned (fish only).	21·9	10·8	0·0	191	(595)	305	231·0	41·6	3·1	0·21	296	245	(905)	124	
230	Pilchards, tinned (whole contents of tin)	18·9	15·4	0·0	221	(573)	290	190·0	38·0	2·6	0·19	269	212	(866)	99	
231	Plaice, raw	15·3	1·8	0·0	79	96	353	16·6	22·0	0·8	—	218	214	83	140	
232	Plaice, steamed ..	18·1	1·9	0·0	92	120	278	37·7	23·9	0·6	—	246	249	112	184	
232a	Plaice, steamed (weighed with bones and skin)	9·8	1·0	0·0	50	65	150	20·4	12·9	0·3	—	133	134	61	99	
233	Plaice, fried	18·0	14·4	7·0	234	124	219	44·9	24·4	0·8	0·15	251	249	174	214	
233a	Plaice, fried (weighed with bones)	11·0	8·8	4·3	142	76	134	27·4	14·9	0·5	0·09	153	152	106	131	
234	Pollack, steamed ..	19·5	0·8	0·0	87	95	438	12·8	32·7	0·5	—	202	238	114	124	
234a	Pollack, steamed (weighed with bones and skin)	16·8	0·7	0·0	75	82	376	11·0	28·1	0·4	—	174	205	98	107	

Fish—*continued*

No.	Food.	Nature of raw material.	Method of cooking.	Nature of edible (analysed) material.	Edible matter, as eaten, expressed as a percentage of the weight as purchased.	g. per 100 g.		
						Water.	Total nitrogen.	Purine nitrogen.
235	Pollack	Steaks	Covered with batter and crumbs and fried	All except bones ..	100	67·5	2·77	0·075
235*a*	Pollack (weighed with bones)	Steaks	Covered with batter and crumbs and fried	All except bones ..	100	62·0	2·55	0·069
236	Pollan	Whole fish without guts	Steamed	Flesh only	59	77·1	3·09	0·082
236*a*	Pollan (weighed with bones and skin)	Whole fish without guts	Steamed	Flesh only	59	47·0	1·88	0·050
237	Pollan	Whole fish without guts	Covered with oatmeal and fried	Flesh and skin ..	65	64·3	3·19	0·096
237*a*	Pollan (weighed with bones)	Whole fish without guts	Covered with oatmeal and fried	Flesh and skin ..	65	46·4	2·29	0·069
238	Prawns	Purchased cooked	.. .. ..	Flesh only	38	70·0	3·62	0·070
238*a*	Prawns (weighed with shells)	Purchased cooked	.. .. ..	Flesh only	38	26·6	1·38	0·027
239	Saithe	Pieces from tail end	Steamed	Flesh only	65	74·8	3·73	0·078
239*a*	Saithe (weighed with bones and skin)	Pieces from tail end	Steamed	Flesh only	65	63·5	3·17	0·066
240	Salmon, fresh	Shoulder cut ..	Steamed	Flesh only	73	65·4	3·21	0·078
240*a*	Salmon, fresh (weighed with bones and skin)	Shoulder cut ..	Steamed	Flesh only	73	53·0	2·60	0·063
241	Salmon	Tinned, as purchased	.. .. ..	All except backbone	98	69·9	3·43	0·101
242	Sardines	Tinned, as purchased	.. .. ..	All, after draining off oil	100	50·7	3·49	0·234
243	Scallops	Flesh only. No shells	Steamed	All	56	73·1	3·71	0·117

Fish—*continued*

No.	Food.	*g. per 100 g.* Protein.	Fat.	Carbohydrate (as glucose).	Calories per 100 g.	*mg. per 100 g.* Na.	K.	Ca.	Mg.	Fe.	Cu.	P.	S.	Cl.	*Acid-base balance, c.c. per 100 g.* $\frac{N}{10}$ Acid.	$\frac{N}{10}$ Alkali.
235	Pollack, fried	16·5	6·9	6·6	157	162	333	128·0	45·4	2·8	—	241	198	275	99	
235*a*	Pollack, fried (weighed with bones)	15·2	6·4	6·1	145	149	306	118·0	41·7	2·6	—	222	182	253	91	
236	Pollan, steamed ..	18·1	2·1	0·0	95	69	373	82·0	23·0	0·9	—	287	220	71	157	
236*a*	Pollan, steamed (weighed with bones and skin)	11·0	1·3	0·0	58	42	227	50·0	14·0	0·5	—	175	134	43	96	
237	Pollan, fried	18·7	12·2	1·7	196	64	390	200·0	25·9	1·2	—	367	228	64	148	
237*a*	Pollan, fried (weighed with bones)	13·5	8·8	1·2	142	46	281	144·0	18·6	0·9	—	264	164	46	106	
238	Prawns	21·2	1·8	0·0	104	(1590)	260	145·0	42·0	1·1	—	349	366	(2550)	307	
238*a*	Prawns (weighed with shells)	8·1	0·7	0·0	40	(605)	99	55·0	16·0	0·4	—	132	139	(970)	117	
239	Saithe, steamed ..	22·6	0·6	0·0	98	97	348	18·6	30·8	0·6	—	250	266	83	184	
239*a*	Saithe, steamed (weighed with bones and skin)	19·2	0·5	0·0	83	83	296	15·8	26·2	0·5	—	213	226	71	156	
240	Salmon, fresh, steamed	19·1	13·0	0·0	199	107	333	28·9	28·7	0·8	—	302	190	64	162	
240*a*	Salmon, fresh, steamed (weighed with bones and skin)	15·5	10·5	0·0	161	87	269	23·4	23·2	0·6	—	245	154	52	131	
241	Salmon, tinned ..	19·7	6·0	0·0	137	(538)	320	66·4	29·8	1·3	0·05	285	235	(865)	201	
242	Sardines, tinned ..	20·4	22·6	0·0	294	(785)	433	409·0	41·3	4·0	0·04	683	283	(1200)	265	
243	Scallops, steamed ..	22·4	1·4	Tr.	105	265	476	115·0	38·3	3·0	—	338	570	410	362	

Fish—*continued*

No.	Food.	*Nature of raw material.*	*Method of cooking.*	*Nature of edible (analysed) material.*	*Edible matter, as eaten, expressed as a percentage of the weight as purchased.*	*g. per 100 g.*		
						Water.	*Total nitrogen.*	*Purine nitrogen.*
244	Shrimps	Purchased cooked ..	.. .. ..	Flesh only	33	62·5	3·80	0·072
244*a*	Shrimps (weighed with shells)	Purchased cooked ..	.. .. ..	Flesh only	33	20·6	1·26	0·024
245	Skate	"Wings" skinned..	Covered with batter and crumbs and fried	All except bones ..	95	55·4	3·09	0·041
245*a*	Skate (weighed with bones)	"Wings" skinned..	Covered with batter and crumbs and fried	All except bones ..	95	46·0	2·56	0·034
246	Smelts	Whole fish without guts	Rolled in flour and fried	All except heads ..	48	34·3	4·29	0·168
246*a*	Smelts (weighed with heads)	Whole fish without guts	Rolled in flour and fried	All except heads ..	48	29·2	3·64	0·143
247	Sole	Body of fish without head or guts	Steamed	Flesh only	57	78·9	2·94	0·053
247*a*	Sole (weighed with bones and skin)	Body of fish without head or guts	Steamed	Flesh only	57	47·3	1·76	0·032
248	Sole	Body of fish without head or guts	Covered with batter and crumbs and fried	All except bones ..	110	53·8	3·32	0·052
248*a*	Sole (weighed with bones)	Body of fish without head or guts	Covered with batter and crumbs and fried	All except bones ..	110	47·3	2·92	0·046
249	Sprats, fresh	Whole fish	Fried in deep fat ..	All except heads ..	59	33·7	3·98	0·125
249*a*	Sprats, fresh (weighed with heads)	Whole fish	Fried in deep fat ..	All except heads ..	59	29·6	3·50	0·110
250	Sprats, smoked	Whole fish	Grilled	Flesh and skin ..	89	45·8	4·18	0·250
250*a*	Sprats, smoked (weighed with heads)	Whole fish	Grilled	Flesh and skin ..	89	40·7	3·72	0·223

Fish—*continued*

No.	Food.	g. per 100 g.			Calories per 100 g.	mg. per 100 g.									Acid-base balance, c.c. per 100 g.	
		Protein.	Fat.	Carbohydrate (as glucose).		Na.	K.	Ca.	Mg.	Fe.	Cu.	P.	S.	Cl.	$\frac{N}{10}$ Acid.	$\frac{N}{10}$ Alkali.
244	Shrimps	22·3	2·4	0·0	114	(3840)	404	320·0	105·0	1·8	0·80	270	340	(5850)	16	
244*a*	Shrimps (weighed with shells)	7·4	0·8	0·0	38	(1260)	133	105·5	34·6	0·6	0·26	89	112	(1930)	5	
245	Skate, fried	15·0	16·4	7·5	242	182	236	19·4	23·2	1·2	—	238	213	266	193	
245*a*	Skate, fried (weighed with bones)	12·4	13·6	6·2	201	151	196	16·1	19·2	1·0	—	198	177	221	160	
246	Smelts, fried	25·0	30·8	5·0	408	148	517	686·0	58·8	3·3	—	535	302	138		39
246*a*	Smelts, fried (weighed with heads)	21·3	26·2	4·3	346	126	438	582·0	50·0	2·8	—	455	257	118		33
247	Sole, steamed	17·6	1·3	0·0	84	110	240	113·0	28·2	0·7	—	270	235	132	169	
247*a*	Sole, steamed (weighed with bones and skin)	10·6	0·8	0·0	50	66	144	68·0	16·9	0·4	—	162	141	79	102	
248	Sole, fried	20·1	18·4	5·4	274	192	236	131·3	27·9	1·4	—	260	265	193	155	
248*a*	Sole, fried (weighed with bones)	17·7	16·2	4·8	241	169	208	115·5	24·5	1·2	—	228	233	170	136	
249	Sprats, fresh, fried ..	22·3	37·9	0·0	444	132	409	707·0	45·8	4·5	—	635	284	182	85	
249*a*	Sprats, fresh, fried (weighed with heads)	19·6	33·4	0·0	390	116	360	620·0	40·3	4·0	—	559	250	160	75	
250	Sprats, smoked, grilled..	25·1	23·2	0·0	319	(845)	483	436·0	40·0	5·7	—	565	275	(1330)	169	
250*a*	Sprats, smoked, grilled (weighed with heads)	22·3	20·6	0·0	284	(751)	430	388·0	35·6	5·1	—	502	245	(1180)	150	

Fish—*continued*

No.	Food.	Nature of raw material.	Method of cooking.	Nature of edible (analysed) material.	Edible matter, as eaten, expressed as a percentage of the weight as purchased.	g. per 100 g. Water.	Total nitrogen.	Purine nitrogen.
251	Stockfish (dried salt cod)	As purchased ..	Soaked in water 24 hours, then boiled	Flesh only	99	64·9	5·20	0·113
251*a*	Stockfish (weighed with bones and skin)	As purchased ..	Soaked in water 24 hours, then boiled	Flesh only	99	53·8	4·32	0·094
252	Sturgeon	Sections from middle of fish, skinned	Steamed	All except bone ..	43	67·5	4·07	0·050
252*a*	Sturgeon (weighed with bones)	Sections from middle of fish, skinned	Steamed	All except bone ..	43	45·8	2·77	0·034
253	Torsk	Middle cut	Steamed	Flesh only	48	74·3	3·75	0·065
253*a*	Torsk (weighed with bones and skin)	Middle cut	Steamed	Flesh only	48	43·9	2·21	0·038
254	Torsk	Slices from middle of fish	Covered with batter and crumbs and fried	Flesh only	70	65·8	3·27	0·064
254*a*	Torsk (weighed with bones and skin)	Slices from middle of fish	Covered with batter and crumbs and fried	Flesh only	70	46·6	2·32	0·045
255	Trout	Whole fish, without guts	Steamed	Flesh only	54	70·6	3·76	0·092
255*a*	Trout (weighed with bones and skin)	Whole fish, without guts	Steamed	Flesh only	54	46·5	2·48	0·061
256	Trout, Sea	Middle cut	Steamed	Flesh only	68	70·9	3·62	0·095
256*a*	Trout, Sea (weighed with bones and skin)	Middle cut	Steamed	Flesh only	68	55·9	2·86	0·075
257	Turbot	Sections from middle of fish	Steamed	Flesh only	56	75·6	3·48	0·064
257*a*	Turbot (weighed with bones and skin)	Sections from middle of fish	Steamed	Flesh only	56	49·8	2·30	0·042
258	Whelks	Purchased cooked ..	.. .. ..	All except shells ..	15	77·5	2·96	0·065
258*a*	Whelks (weighed with shells)	Purchased cooked ..	.. .. ..	All except shells ..	15	11·6	0·44	0·010

Fish—*continued*

No.	Food.	Protein. (g. per 100 g.)	Fat. (g. per 100 g.)	Carbohydrate (as glucose). (g. per 100 g.)	Calories per 100 g.	Na. (mg. per 100 g.)	K.	Ca.	Mg.	Fe.	Cu.	P.	S.	Cl.	$\frac{N}{10}$ Acid. (Acid-base balance, c.c. per 100 g.)	$\frac{N}{10}$ Alkali.
251	Stockfish, boiled ..	32·0	0·9	0·0	140	(396)	31	22·4	35·0	1·8	—	163	372	(670)	307	
251*a*	Stockfish, boiled (weighed with bones and skin)	26·6	0·8	0·0	116	(329)	26	18·6	29·0	1·5	—	135	309	(556)	255	
252	Sturgeon, steamed ..	24·7	5·7	0·0	154	108	235	15·2	18·5	2·0	—	263	291	138	261	
252*a*	Sturgeon, steamed (weighed with bones)	16·8	3·9	0·0	105	74	160	10·4	12·6	1·4	—	179	198	94	178	
253	Torsk, steamed	22·4	0·7	0·0	99	74	386	27·0	26·4	1·0	—	283	278	101	218	
253*a*	Torsk, steamed (weighed with bones and skin)	13·2	0·4	0·0	58	44	228	15·9	15·6	0·6	—	167	164	60	129	
254	Torsk, fried	19·3	4·3	7·8	148	93	372	64·8	24·9	0·6	—	298	234	153	193	
254*a*	Torsk, fried (weighed with bones and skin)	13·7	3·1	5·5	105	66	264	45·9	17·7	0·4	—	212	166	109	137	
255	Trout, steamed	22·3	4·5	0·0	133	88	374	35·8	30·9	1·0	—	270	218	70	152	
255*a*	Trout, steamed (weighed with bones and skin)	14·7	3·0	0·0	88	58	246	23·6	20·4	0·7	—	178	144	46	100	
256	Trout, Sea, steamed ..	21·1	4·8	0·0	131	207	314	12·4	30·1	1·0	—	290	259	261	221	
256*a*	Trout, Sea, steamed (weighed with bones and skin)	16·6	3·8	0·0	104	163	248	9·8	23·8	0·8	—	229	204	206	174	
257	Turbot, steamed ..	20·7	1·6	0·0	100	90	255	13·5	23·9	0·5	—	188	247	142	184	
257*a*	Turbot, steamed (weighed with bones and skin)	13·6	1·1	0·0	66	59	168	8·9	15·8	0·3	—	124	163	94	121	
258	Whelks	17·8	1·9	Tr.	91	(265)	316	54·0	160·0	6·2	—	227	448	(585)	235	
258*a*	Whelks (weighed with shells)	2·7	0·8	Tr.	14	(40)	47	8·1	24·0	0·9	—	34	67	(88)	35	

Fish—*continued*

No.	*Food.*	*Nature of raw material.*	*Method of cooking.*	*Nature of edible (analysed) material.*	*Edible matter, as eaten, expressed as a percentage of the weight as purchased.*	*g. per 100 g.*		
						Water.	*Total nitrogen.*	*Purine nitrogen.*
259	Whitebait	Whole fish	Rolled in flour and fried	All	77	23·5	3·12	0·335
260	Whiting	Body of fish without head or guts	Steamed	Flesh only	57	76·9	3·35	0·090
260*a*	Whiting (weighed with bones and skin)	Body of fish without head or guts	Steamed	Flesh only	57	52·2	2·28	0·061
261	Whiting	Body of fish without head or guts	Covered with batter and crumbs and fried	All except bones ..	102	63·0	2·90	0·094
261*a*	Whiting (weighed with bones)	Body of fish without head or guts	Covered with batter and crumbs and fried	All except bones ..	102	56·8	2·61	0·085
262	Winkles, edible portion ..	Purchased cooked ..	Probably boiled in salt water	All except shells ..	19	79·1	2·45	0·066
262*a*	Winkles (weighed with shells)	Purchased cooked ..	Probably boiled in salt water	All except shells ..	19	15·1	0·47	0·013
263	Winkles	In shells as purchased	Boiled in fresh water	All except shells ..	15	76·8	2·90	0·070
263*a*	Winkles (weighed with shells)	In shells as purchased	Boiled in fresh water	All except shells ..	15	11·5	0·44	0·011
264	Witch	Body of fish without head, fins or guts	Steamed	Flesh only	48	77·7	3·18	0·053
264*a*	Witch (weighed with bones and skin)	Body of fish without head, fins or guts	Steamed	Flesh only	48	46·5	1·91	0·032
265	Witch	Body of fish without head, fins or guts	Covered with batter and crumbs and fried	All except bones ..	113	58·1	2·96	0·055
265*a*	Witch (weighed with bones)	Body of fish without head, fins or guts	Covered with batter and crumbs and fried	All except bones ..	113	48·9	2·49	0·046

Fish—*continued*

No.	Food.	*g. per 100 g.* Protein.	Fat.	Carbohydrate (as glucose).	Calories per 100 g.	*mg. per 100 g.* Na.	K.	Ca.	Mg.	Fe.	Cu.	P.	S.	Cl.	*Acid-base balance, c.c. per 100 g.* $\frac{N}{10}$ Acid.	$\frac{N}{10}$ Alkali.
259	Whitebait, fried ..	18·3	47·5	5·3	537	225	112	859·0	50·3	5·1	—	856	269	325	214	
260	Whiting, steamed ..	19·9	0·9	0·0	90	127	299	42·0	28·3	1·0	—	189	307	93	164	
260*a*	Whiting, steamed (weighed with bones and skin)	13·5	0·6	0·0	61	86	203	28·6	19·2	0·7	—	128	208	63	112	
261	Whiting, fried	17·3	10·3	7·0	193	199	317	47·7	32·5	0·7	—	258	267	194	169	
261*a*	Whiting, fried (weighed with bones and skin)	15·6	9·3	6·3	174	179	285	42·9	29·3	0·6	—	233	240	175	152	
262	Winkles, boiled in salt water	15·2	1·4	Tr.	75	(1140)	154	136·0	358·0	15·0	—	219	377	(1800)		20
262*a*	Winkles, boiled in salt water (weighed with shells)	2·9	0·3	Tr.	14	(218)	29	25·8	68·0	2·9	—	42	72	(342)		4
263	Winkles, boiled in fresh water	17·6	2·6	Tr.	96	266	211	165·0	414·0	17·1	—	277	446	500	1	
263*a*	Winkles, boiled in fresh water (weighed with shells)	2·6	0·4	Tr.	14	40	32	24·8	62·0	2·6	—	42	67	75	<1	
264	Witch, steamed	19·0	1·1	0·0	88	136	304	30·1	24·1	0·9	—	233	252	123	170	
264*a*	Witch, steamed (weighed with bones and skin)	11·4	0·7	0·0	53	82	182	18·1	14·4	0·5	—	140	151	74	102	
265	Witch, fried	17·6	14·1	7·9	233	176	300	52·2	24·4	0·8	—	187	235	187	121	
265*a*	Witch, fried (weighed with bones and skin)	14·8	11·8	6·6	196	148	252	43·8	20·5	0·7	—	157	197	157	102	

Fruit

No.	Food.	Description.	Nature of edible (analysed) material.	Edible matter, as eaten, expressed as a percentage of the weight as purchased.	g. per 100 g.				
					Water.	Unavailable carbohydrate.	Sugar (as monosaccharides).	Starch (as glucose).	Total nitrogen.
266	Apples, Empire eating ..	Raw	Flesh only, no skin or core	75	84·1	1·7	12·2	Tr.	0·04
266*a*	Apples, Empire eating (weighed with skin and core)	Raw	Flesh only, no skin or core	75	63·1	1·3	9·2	Tr.	0·03
267	Apples, English eating ..	Raw	Flesh only, no skin or core	79	84·5	2·2	11·4	0·3	0·04
267*a*	Apples, English eating (weighed with skin and core)	Raw	Flesh only, no skin or core	79	66·8	1·7	9·0	0·2	0·03
268	Apples, English cooking ..	Raw	Flesh only, no skin or core	81	85·6	2·4	9·2	0·4	0·05
269	Apples, English cooking ..	Baked without sugar	Flesh only, no skin (cored before cooking)	70	85·0	2·5	9·6	0·4	0·05
269*a*	Apples, English cooking (weighed with skin)	Baked without sugar	Flesh only, no skin (cored before cooking)	70	68·0	2·0	7·7	0·3	0·04
270	Apples, English cooking ..	Stewed without sugar	Flesh and juice (peeled and cored before cooking)	177	93·4	1·1	4·2	0·2	0·02
271	Apricots, fresh	Raw	Flesh and skin, no stones ..	92	86·6	2·1	6·7	0·0	0·09
271*a*	Apricots, fresh (weighed with stones)	Raw	Flesh and skin, no stones ..	92	79·6	1·9	6·2	0·0	0·08
272	Apricots, dried	Raw	All	100	14·7	24·0	43·4	0·0	0·76
273	Apricots, dried	Stewed without sugar	Fruit and juice	241	64·6	10·0	18·0	0·0	0·32
274	Apricots	Tinned in syrup ..	Fruit and syrup as purchased	100	79·8	1·3	15·7	0·0	0·08
275	Avocado pears	Raw	Flesh only, no skin or stone	62	81·3	2·0	2·5	0·0	0·17
276	Bananas	Raw	Flesh only, no skin ..	59	70·7	3·4	16·2	3·0	0·18
276*a*	Bananas (weighed with skin)	Raw	Flesh only, no skin ..	59	41·6	2·0	9·6	1·8	0·11
277	Blackberries	Raw	Whole fruit	100	82·0	7·3	6·4	0·0	0·20

Fruit—*continued*

No.	Food.	g. per 100 g. Protein (N × 6·25).	Fat.	Available carbohydrate (as monosaccharides).	Calories per 100 g.	mg. per 100 g. Na.	K.	Ca.	Mg.	Fe.	Cu.	P.	S.	Cl.	Acid-base balance, c.c. per 100 g. N/10 Acid.	N/10 Alkali.
266	Apples, Empire eating ..	0·3	Tr.	12·2	47	2·7	116	3·6	5·0	0·29	0·14	6·8	3·7	<1·0		30
266a	Apples, Empire eating (weighed with skin and core)	0·2	Tr.	9·2	35	2·0	87	2·7	3·8	0·22	0·11	5·1	2·8	<1·0		23
267	Apples, English eating	0·3	Tr.	11·7	45	2·0	120	3·5	4·3	0·29	0·07	8·5	7·6	2·0		26
267a	Apples, English eating (weighed with skin and core)	0·2	Tr.	9·3	36	1·6	95	2·8	3·4	0·23	0·06	6·7	6·0	1·6		21
268	Apples, cooking, raw ..	0·3	Tr.	9·6	37	2·1	123	3·6	2·9	0·29	0·09	16·2	2·9	4·6		23
269	Apples, cooking, baked	0·3	Tr.	10·0	39	2·2	128	3·7	3·0	0·30	0·09	16·8	3·0	4·8		24
269a	Apples, cooking, baked (weighed with skin)	0·2	Tr.	8·0	31	1·8	102	3·0	2·4	0·24	0·07	13·4	2·4	3·8		19
270	Apples, cooking, stewed without sugar	0·1	Tr.	4·4	17	0·1	56	1·7	1·3	0·13	0·04	7·4	1·3	2·1		11
271	Apricots, fresh	0·6	Tr.	6·7	28	<1·0	320	17·2	12·3	0·37	0·12	21·3	6·1	<1·0		84
271a	Apricots, fresh (weighed with stones)	0·6	Tr.	6·2	26	<1·0	294	15·8	11·3	0·34	0·11	19·6	5·6	<1·0		77
272	Apricots, dried, raw ..	4·8	Tr.	43·4	183	56·4	1880	92·4	65·2	4·09	0·27	118·0	164·0	34·5		419
273	Apricots, dried, stewed without sugar	2·0	Tr.	18·0	76	23·4	783	38·4	27·1	1·70	0·11	49·0	68·1	14·3		174
274	Apricots, tinned in syrup	0·5	Tr.	15·7	61	0·9	256	12·0	7·2	0·70	0·05	13·0	1·0	1·5		69
275	Avocado pears	1·1	8·0	2·5	88	16·0	396	15·3	29·4	0·53	0·21	30·8	19·4	5·9		107
276	Bananas	1·1	Tr.	19·2	77	1·2	348	6·8	41·9	0·41	0·16	28·1	13·0	78·5		79
276a	Bananas (weighed with skin)	0·7	Tr.	11·3	45	0·7	206	4·0	24·7	0·24	0·09	16·6	7·7	46·3		47
277	Blackberries, raw ..	1·3	Tr.	6·4	30	3·7	208	63·3	29·5	0·85	0·12	23·8	9·2	22·1		84

Fruit—*continued*

No.	Food.	Description.	Nature of edible (analysed) material.	Edible matter, as eaten, expressed as a percentage of the weight as purchased.	g. per 100 g.				
					Water.	Unavailable carbohydrate.	Sugar (as monosaccharides).	Starch (as glucose).	Total nitrogen.
278	Blackberries	Stewed without sugar	Fruit and juice	200	91·0	3·7	3·2	0·0	0·10
279	Cherries, eating	Raw..	Flesh and skin, no stalks or stones	87	81·5	1·7	11·9	0·0	0·09
279*a*	Cherries, eating (weighed with stones)	Raw..	Flesh and skin, no stalks or stones	87	71·0	1·5	10·4	0·0	0·08
280	Cherries, cooking	Raw..	Flesh and skin, no stalks or stones	84	79·8	1·7	11·6	0·0	0·09
280*a*	Cherries, cooking (weighed with stones)	Raw..	Flesh and skin, no stalks or stones	84	67·0	1·4	9·8	0·0	0·08
281	Cherries, cooking (weighed with stones)	Stewed without sugar	Fruit and juice, no stones ..	238	86·2	0·6	4·1	0·0	0·03
282	Cranberries	Raw..	Whole fruit	100	87·0	4·2	3·5	0·0	0·06
283	Currants, black	Raw..	Whole fruit, no stalks ..	98	77·4	8·7	6·6	0·0	0·15
284	Currants, black	Stewed without sugar	Fruit and juice	141	84·3	6·1	4·6	0·0	0·10
285	Currants, red	Raw..	Whole fruit, no stalks ..	97	82·8	8·2	4·4	0·0	0·18
286	Currants, red	Stewed without sugar	Fruit and juice ..	133	87·5	6·0	3·2	0·0	0·13
287	Currants, white	Raw..	Whole fruit, no stalks ..	96	83·3	6·8	5·6	0·0	0·20
288	Currants, dried	Raw..	Whole fruit	100	22·0	6·5	63·1	0·0	0·27
289	Custard apple	Raw..	Flesh only, no skin or seeds	71	73·3	3·2	18·1	0·0	0·33
290	Damsons	Raw..	Flesh and skin, no stalks or stones	90	77·5	4·1	9·6	0·0	0·08
290*a*	Damsons (weighed with stones)	Raw..	Flesh and skin, no stalks or stones	90	69·8	3·7	8·6	0·0	0·07
291	Damsons (weighed with stones)	Stewed without sugar	Fruit and juice, no stones	131	76·9	2·8	6·6	0·0	0·06

Fruit—*continued*

No.	Food.	g. per 100 g. Protein (N × 6·25).	Fat.	Available carbohydrate (as monosaccharides).	Calories per 100 g.	mg. per 100 g. Na.	K.	Ca.	Mg.	Fe.	Cu.	P.	S.	Cl.	Acid-base balance. c.c. per 100 g. $\frac{N}{10}$ Acid.	$\frac{N}{10}$ Alkali.
278	Blackberries, stewed without sugar	0·7	Tr.	3·2	15	1·9	104	32·1	14·8	0·43	0·06	11·9	4·6	11·1		42
279	Cherries, eating	0·6	Tr.	11·9	47	2·8	275	15·9	9·6	0·38	0·07	16·8	6·8	<1·0		73
279a	Cherries, eating (weighed with stones)	0·5	Tr.	10·4	40	2·4	239	13·8	8·4	0·33	0·06	14·6	5·9	<1·0		64
280	Cherries, cooking, raw ..	0·6	Tr.	11·6	46	4·1	305	20·1	11·6	0·31	0·10	20·8	7·9	<1·0		81
280a	Cherries, cooking, raw (weighed with stones)	0·5	Tr.	9·8	39	3·4	256	16·9	9·8	0·26	0·08	17·5	6·6	<1·0		68
281	Cherries, stewed without sugar (weighed with stones)	0·2	Tr.	4·1	17	1·5	108	7·1	4·1	0·11	0·04	7·4	2·8	<1·0		29
282	Cranberries	0·4	Tr.	3·5	15	1·8	119	14·7	8·4	1·11	0·14	11·2	11·1	<1·0		32
283	Currants, black, raw ..	0·9	Tr.	6·6	29	2·7	372	60·3	17·1	1·27	0·14	43·2	33·1	14·8		88
284	Currants, black, stewed without sugar	0·6	Tr.	4·6	20	1·9	259	42·1	11·9	0·89	0·10	30·1	23·1	10·3		61
285	Currants, red, raw ..	1·1	Tr.	4·4	21	2·3	275	35·8	12·8	1·22	0·12	29·5	28·6	14·0		59
286	Currants, red, stewed without sugar	0·8	Tr.	3·2	16	1·7	200	26·1	9·3	0·89	0·09	21·4	20·8	10·2		43
287	Currants, white	1·3	Tr.	5·6	26	1·5	291	22·4	12·7	0·93	0·14	28·0	23·6	10·7		61
288	Currants, dried	1·7	Tr.	63·1	244	19·5	708	95·2	36·2	1·82	0·48	40·4	30·8	15·7		218
289	Custard apple	2·1	Tr.	18·1	77	13·8	578	12·0	23·9	0·53	0·15	51·0	26·7	40·0		119
290	Damsons, raw	0·5	Tr.	9·6	38	2·2	290	23·5	11·0	0·41	0·08	16·4	6·4	<1·0		82
290a	Damsons, raw (weighed with stones)	0·5	Tr.	8·6	34	2·0	261	21·2	9·9	0·37	0·07	14·8	5·8	<1·0		74
291	Damsons, stewed without sugar (weighed with stones)	0·3	Tr.	6·6	26	1·5	199	16·2	7·6	0·28	0·06	11·3	4·4	<1·0		56

Fruit—*continued*

No.	Food.	Description.	Nature of edible (analysed) material.	Edible matter, as eaten, expressed as a percentage of the weight as purchased.	g. per 100 g.				
					Water.	Unavailable carbohydrate.	Sugar (as monosaccharides).	Starch (as glucose).	Total nitrogen.
292	Dates	Dried, as purchased	Flesh and skin, no stones	86	14·6	8·7	63·9	0·0	0·32
292*a*	Dates (weighed with stones)	Dried, as purchased	Flesh and skin, no stones	86	12·6	7·5	54·9	0·0	0·28
293	Figs, green	Raw	Whole fruit, no stalks	98	84·6	2·5	9·5	0·0	0·21
294	Figs, dried	Raw	Whole fruit	100	16·8	18·5	52·9	0·0	0·57
295	Figs, dried	Stewed without sugar	Fruit and juice	176	52·8	10·5	30·0	0·0	0·32
296	Fruit salad	Tinned in syrup	Fruit and syrup, as purchased	100	77·6	1·1	18·5	0·0	0·04
297	Gooseberries, green	Raw	Flesh, skin and pips, no "tops" or "tails"	99	89·9	3·2	3·4	0·0	0·18
298	Gooseberries, green	Stewed without sugar	Fruit and juice	198	95·0	1·6	1·7	0·0	0·09
299	Gooseberries, ripe	Raw	Flesh, skin and pips, no "tops" or "tails"	99	83·7	3·5	9·2	0·0	0·09
300	Grapes, black	Raw	Flesh only, no skin, pips or stalks	81	80·7	0·4	15·5	0·0	0·09
300*a*	Grapes, black (whole grapes weighed)	Raw	Flesh only, no skin, pips or stalks	81	65·2	0·3	13·0	0·0	0·08
301	Grapes, white	Raw	Flesh and skin, no pips or stalks	95	79·3	0·9	16·1	0·0	0·10
301*a*	Grapes, white (whole grapes weighed)	Raw	Flesh and skin, no pips or stalks	95	75·5	0·9	15·3	0·0	0·10
302	Grapefruit	Raw	Flesh only, no skin, pith or pips	48	90·7	0·6	5·3	0·0	0·10
302*a*	Grapefruit (whole fruit weighed)	Raw	Flesh only, no skin, pith or pips	48	43·5	0·3	2·5	0·0	0·05

Fruit—*continued*

No.	Food.	Protein (N × 6·25). g. per 100 g.	Fat. g. per 100 g.	Available carbohydrate (as monosaccharides). g. per 100 g.	Calories per 100 g.	Na. mg. per 100 g.	K.	Ca.	Mg.	Fe.	Cu.	P.	S.	Cl.	$\frac{N}{10}$ Acid. Acid-base balance, c.c. per 100 g.	$\frac{N}{10}$ Alkali
292	Dates	2·0	Tr.	63·9	248	4·8	754	67·9	58·5	1·61	0·21	63·8	51·0	290·0		124
292*a*	Dates (weighed with stones)	1·7	Tr.	54·9	214	4·1	649	58·3	50·3	1·38	0·18	54·8	43·8	249·0		107
293	Figs, green	1·3	Tr.	9·5	41	1·6	268	34·2	20·0	0·42	0·06	32·2	12·9	18·4		69
294	Figs, dried, raw ..	3·6	Tr.	52·9	214	86·7	1010	284·0	92·3	4·17	0·24	91·5	80·8	166·0		361
295	Figs, dried, stewed without sugar	2·0	Tr.	30·0	122	49·3	576	161·5	52·5	2·37	0·14	52·0	45·9	94·2		205
296	Fruit salad, tinned in syrup	0·3	Tr.	18·5	70	2·3	116	8·4	7·7	3·45	0·03	9·6	1·8	3·2		33
297	Gooseberries, green, raw	1·1	Tr.	3·4	17	1·9	210	28·3	7·1	0·32	0·13	33·9	15·9	6·5		41
298	Gooseberries, green, stewed without sugar	0·6	Tr.	1·7	9	1·0	105	14·2	3·6	0·16	0·07	17·0	8·0	3·3		21
299	Gooseberries, ripe ..	0·6	Tr.	9·2	37	1·2	170	18·5	8·6	0·58	0·15	19·0	13·5	10·7		37
300	Grapes, black	0·6	Tr.	15·5	60	1·7	316	4·2	4·0	0·34	0·08	16·1	7·4	<1·0		72
300*a*	Grapes, black (whole grapes weighed)	0·5	Tr.	13·0	51	1·4	265	3·5	3·4	0·29	0·07	13·5	6·2	<1·0		58
301	Grapes, white	0·6	Tr.	16·1	63	1·6	250	19·1	6·6	0·34	0·10	21·9	9·1	<1·0		60
301*a*	Grapes, white (whole grapes weighed)	0·6	Tr.	15·3	60	1·5	237	18·1	6·3	0·32	0·10	20·8	8·7	<1·0		57
302	Grapefruit	0·6	Tr.	5·3	22	1·4	234	17·1	10·4	0·26	0·06	15·6	5·1	1·3		64
302*a*	Grapefruit (whole fruit weighed)	0·3	Tr.	2·5	11	0·7	112	8·2	5·0	0·13	0·03	7·5	2·5	0·6		31

Fruit—*continued*

No.	Food.	Description.	Nature of edible (analysed) material.	Edible matter, as eaten, expressed as a percentage of the weight as purchased.	g. per 100 g.				
					Water.	Unavailable carbohydrate.	Sugar (as monosaccharides).	Starch (as glucose).	Total nitrogen.
303	Greengages	Raw..	Flesh and skin, no stones or stalks	95	78·2	2·6	11·8	0·0	0·12
303*a*	Greengages (weighed with stones)	Raw..	Flesh and skin, no stones or stalks	95	74·4	2·5	11·2	0·0	0·11
304	Greengages (weighed with stones)	Stewed without sugar	Fruit and juice, no stones	147	82·6	1·7	7·6	0·0	0·08
305	Lemons, whole	Raw..	Whole fruit, including skin, no pips	99	85·2	5·2	3·2	0·0	0·12
306	Lemon juice	Raw..	Strained juice	36	91·3	0·0	1·6	0·0	0·05
307	Loganberries	Raw..	Whole fruit	100	85·0	6·2	3·4	0·0	0·17
308	Loganberries	Tinned in syrup ..	Fruit and syrup as purchased	100	66·3	3·3	26·2	0·0	0·10
309	Medlars	Raw..	Flesh only, no skin or stones	81	74·5	10·2	10·6	0·0	0·08
309*a*	Medlars (weighed with skin and stones)	Raw..	Flesh only, no skin or stones	81	60·2	8·3	8·6	0·0	0·06
310	Melons, Cantaloupe ..	Raw..	Flesh only, no skin or pips	59	93·6	1·0	5·3	0·0	0·16
310*a*	Melons, Cantaloupe (weighed with skin)	Raw..	Flesh only, no skin or pips	59	58·6	0·6	3·3	0·0	0·10
311	Melons, yellow	Raw..	Flesh only, no skin or pips	59	94·2	0·9	5·0	0·0	0·10
311*a*	Melons, yellow (weighed with skin)	Raw..	Flesh only, no skin or pips	59	59·0	0·6	3·1	0·0	0·06
312	Mulberries	Raw..	Whole fruit	100	85·0	1·7	8·1	0·0	0·21
313	Nectarines	Raw..	Flesh and skin, no stones	92	80·2	2·4	12·4	0·0	0·15
313*a*	Nectarines (weighed with stones)	Raw..	Flesh and skin, no stones	92	74·0	2·2	11·4	0·0	0·14

Fruit—*continued*

No.	Food.	Protein (N × 6·25). g. per 100 g.	Fat. g. per 100 g.	Available carbohydrate (as monosaccharides). g. per 100 g.	Calories per 100 g.	Na. mg. per 100 g.	K.	Ca.	Mg.	Fe.	Cu.	P.	S.	Cl.	Acid-base balance, c.c per 100 g. N/10 Acid.	N/10 Alkali.
303	Greengages	0·8	Tr.	11·8	48	1·4	305	16·8	7·7	0·37	0·08	22·6	3·0	1·0		77
303*a*	Greengages (weighed with stones)	0·8	Tr.	11·2	45	1·3	290	16·0	7·3	0·35	0·08	21·5	2·9	1·0		73
304	Greengages, stewed without sugar (weighed with stones)	0·5	Tr.	7·6	31	0·9	196	10·8	5·0	0·24	0·05	14·6	1·9	0·6		50
305	Lemons, whole	0·8	Tr.	3·2	15	6·0	163	107·0	11·6	0·35	0·26	20·7	12·3	5·1		85
306	Lemon juice	0·3	Tr.	1·6	7	1·5	142	8·4	6·6	0·14	0·13	10·3	2·0	2·6		38
307	Loganberries	1·1	Tr.	3·4	17	2·5	257	35·1	25·0	1·37	0·14	24·3	18·1	15·8		74
308	Loganberries, tinned in syrup	0·6	Tr.	26·2	101	1·2	97	17·6	11·3	2·88	0·04	23·0	3·0	4·6		25
309	Medlars	0·5	Tr.	10·6	42	6·0	246	30·1	10·5	0·49	0·17	28·0	16·6	3·1		60
309*a*	Medlars (weighed with skin and stones)	0·4	Tr.	8·6	34	4·9	200	24·4	8·5	0·40	0·14	22·7	13·5	2·5		49
310	Melons, Cantaloupe ..	1·0	Tr.	5·3	24	13·5	319	19·1	20·1	0·81	0·04	30·4	11·7	43·5		75
310*a*	Melons, Cantaloupe (weighed with skin)	0·6	Tr.	3·3	15	8·5	200	11·9	12·6	0·51	0·03	19·0	7·3	27·2		47
311	Melons, yellow	0·6	Tr.	5·0	21	19·5	222	13·8	13·3	0·24	0·04	8·7	6·3	45·0		61
311*a*	Melons, yellow (weighed with skin)	0·4	Tr.	3·1	13	12·2	139	8·6	8·3	0·15	0·03	5·4	3·9	28·2		38
312	Mulberries	1·3	Tr.	8·1	36	2·1	257	35·7	15·1	1·57	0·06	47·7	8·8	3·7		60
313	Nectarines	0·9	Tr.	12·4	50	9·1	268	3·9	12·6	0·46	0·06	23·9	10·0	4·7		62
313*a*	Nectarines (weighed with stones)	0·8	Tr.	11·4	46	8·4	247	3·6	11·6	0·42	0·06	22·0	9·2	4·3		57

Fruit—*continued*

No.	Food.	Description.	Nature of edible (analysed) material.	Edible matter, as eaten, expressed as a percentage of the weight as purchased.	g. per 100 g.				
					Water.	Unavailable carbohydrate.	Sugar (as monosaccharides).	Starch (as glucose).	Total nitrogen.
314	Olives	Bottled in brine ..	Flesh and skin, no stones ..	80	76·5	4·4	0·0	0·0	0·14
314*a*	Olives (weighed with stones)	Bottled in brine ..	Flesh and skin, no stones ..	80	61·1	3·5	0·0	0·0	0·11
315	Oranges	Raw..	Flesh only, no peel or pips	75	86·1	2·0	8·5	0·0	0·13
315*a*	Oranges((weighed with peel and pips)	Raw..	Flesh only, no peel or pips	75	64·8	1·5	6·4	0·0	0·10
316	Orange juice	Raw..	Strained juice	46	87·7	0·0	9·4	0·0	0·10
317	Passion fruit	Raw..	Flesh and seeds, no skin ..	42	73·3	15·9	6·2	0·0	0·44
317*a*	Passion fruit (weighed with skin)	Raw..	Flesh and seeds, no skin ..	42	30·8	6·7	2·6	0·0	0·18
318	Peaches, fresh	Raw..	Flesh and skin, no stones ..	87	86·2	1·4	9·1	0·0	0·10
318*a*	Peaches, fresh (weighed with stones)	Raw..	Flesh and skin, no stones ..	87	75·1	1·2	7·9	0·0	0·09
319	Peaches, dried	Raw..	All	100	15·5	14·3	53·0	0·0	0·55
320	Peaches, dried	Stewed without sugar	Fruit and juice	294	71·3	4·9	18·0	0·0	0·19
321	Peaches	Tinned in syrup ..	Fruit and syrup as purchased	100	80·0	1·0	17·2	0·0	0·06
322	Pears, Empire eating ..	Raw..	Flesh only, no skin or core	69	83·0	2·5	10·8	0·0	0·04
322*a*	Pears, Empire eating (weighed with skin and core)	Raw..	Flesh only, no skin or core	69	57·2	1·7	7·5	0·0	0·03
323	Pears, English eating ..	Raw..	Flesh only, no skin or core	75	83·4	2·1	10·4	0·0	0·03
323*a*	Pears, English eating (weighed with skin and core)	Raw..	Flesh only, no skin or core	75	62·5	1·6	7·8	0·0	0·02
324	Pears, English cooking ..	Raw..	Flesh only, no skin or core	77	83·0	2·9	9·3	Tr.	0·04
325	Pears, English cooking ..	Stewed without sugar	Flesh and juice (peeled and cored before cooking)	110	88·4	2·0	6·5	Tr.	0·03
326	Pears	Tinned in syrup ..	Fruit and syrup as purchased	100	79·8	1·7	16·4	0·0	0·06

Fruit—*continued*

No.	Food.	*g. per 100 g.* Protein (N × 6·25).	Fat.	Available carbohydrate (as monosaccharides).	Calories per 100 g.	*mg. per 100 g.* Na.	K.	Ca.	Mg.	Fe.	Cu.	P.	S.	Cl.	*Acid-base balance, c.c. per 100 g.* $\frac{N}{10}$ Acid.	$\frac{N}{10}$ Alkali.
314	Olives (in brine) ..	0·9	11·0	0·0	106	(2250)	91	61·2	21·8	1·03	0·23	16·8	35·6	(3750)	38	
314*a*	Olives (in brine) (weighed with stones)	0·7	8·8	0·0	85	(1800)	73	49·0	17·5	0·83	0·18	13·4	28·5	(3000)	30	
315	Oranges	0·8	Tr.	8·5	35	2·9	197	41·3	12·9	0·33	0·07	23·7	9·0	3·2		61
315*a*	Oranges (weighed with peel and pips)	0·6	Tr.	6·4	27	2·2	148	31·0	9·7	0·25	0·05	17·8	6·8	2·4		46
316	Orange juice	0·6	Tr.	9·4	38	1·7	179	11·5	11·5	0·30	0·05	21·7	4·6	1·2		45
317	Passion fruit	2·8	Tr.	6·2	35	28·4	348	15·6	38·6	1·12	0·12	54·2	18·7	36·6		85
317*a*	Passion fruit (weighed with skin)	1·2	Tr.	2·6	15	11·9	146	6·5	16·2	0·47	0·05	22·8	7·8	15·4		36
318	Peaches, fresh	0·6	Tr.	9·1	37	2·7	259	4·8	7·9	0·38	0·05	18·5	5·7	<1·0		61
318*a*	Peaches, fresh (weighed with stones)	0·5	Tr.	7·9	32	2·4	225	4·2	6·9	0·33	0·04	16·1	5·0	<1·0		53
319	Peaches, dried, raw ..	3·4	Tr.	53·0	213	6·0	1100	35·6	54·1	6·75	0·63	116·0	240·0	10·5		121
320	Peaches, dried, stewed without sugar	1·2	Tr.	18·0	72	2·0	376	12·1	18·4	2·29	0·21	39·4	81·5	3·6		41
321	Peaches, tinned in syrup	0·4	Tr.	17·2	66	1·4	151	3·5	6·3	1·93	0·06	10·0	1·0	4·2		38
322	Pears, Empire eating ..	0·3	Tr.	10·8	42	2·3	129	8·0	9·3	0·19	0·20	9·9	5·6	<1·0		36
322*a*	Pears, Empire eating, (weighed with skin and core)	0·2	Tr.	7·5	29	1·6	89	5·5	6·4	0·13	0·14	6·8	3·9	<1·0		25
323	Pears, English eating ..	0·2	Tr.	10·4	40	2·3	127	6·9	5·1	0·22	0·09	9·5	2·7	<1·0		34
323*a*	Pears, English eating .. (weighed with skin and core)	0·2	Tr.	7·8	30	1·7	95	5·2	3·8	0·17	0·07	7·1	2·0	<1·0		26
324	Pears, cooking, raw ..	0·3	Tr.	9·3	36	2·5	100	7·1	4·2	0·16	0·11	14·6	3·4	1·5		22
325	Pears, cooking, stewed without sugar	0·2	Tr.	6·5	25	1·7	70	5·0	2·9	0·11	0·08	10·2	2·4	1·1		15
326	Pears, tinned in syrup ..	0·4	Tr.	16·4	63	1·4	90	5·3	5·9	1·75	0·04	5·3	1·3	2·8		26

Fruit—*continued*

No.	Food.	Description.	Nature of edible (analysed) material.	Edible matter, as eaten, expressed as a percentage of the weight as purchased.	g. per 100 g.				
					Water.	Unavailable carbohydrate.	Sugar (as monosaccharides).	Starch (as glucose).	Total nitrogen.
327	Pineapple, fresh	Raw	Flesh only, no skin or core	53	84·3	1·2	11·6	0·0	0·08
328	Pineapple	Tinned in syrup ..	Fruit and syrup as purchased	100	80·8	0·9	16·5	0·0	0·04
329	Plums, Victoria dessert ..	Raw..	Flesh and skin, no stones or stalks	94	84·1	2·1	9·6	0·0	0·09
329*a*	Plums, Victoria dessert (weighed with stones)	Raw..	Flesh and skin, no stones or stalks	94	79·1	2·0	9·0	0·0	0·08
330	Plums, cooking	Raw..	Flesh and skin, no stones or stalks	91	85·1	2·5	6·2	0·0	0·09
330*a*	Plums, cooking (weighed with stones)	Raw..	Flesh and skin, no stones or stalks	91	77·5	2·3	5·6	0·0	0·08
331	Plums, cooking (weighed with stones)	Stewed without sugar	Fruit and juice, no stones..	140	83·9	1·6	4·0	0·0	0·06
332	Pomegranate juice ..	Raw..	Juice only	56	85·4	0·0	11·6	0·0	0·03
333	Prunes, dried	Raw..	Flesh and skin, no stones ..	83	23·3	16·1	40·3	0·0	0·39
333*a*	Prunes, dried (weighed with stones)	Raw..	Flesh and skin, no stones ..	83	19·3	13·4	33·5	0·0	0·32
334	Prunes, dried (weighed with stones)	Stewed without sugar	Fruit and juice, no stones..	216	62·6	6·2	15·5	0·0	0·15
335	Quinces	Raw..	Flesh only, no skin or core	69	84·2	6·4	6·3	Tr.	0·05
336	Raisins, dried	Raw..	Flesh and skin, no stones ..	92	21·5	6·8	64·4	0·0	0·17
337	Raspberries	Raw..	Whole fruit	100	83·2	7·4	5·6	0·0	0·14
338	Raspberries	Stewed without sugar	Fruit and juice	100	88·6	5·0	3·8	0·0	0·10
339	Rhubarb	Raw..	Stems only	67	94·2	2·6	1·0	0·0	0·10
340	Rhubarb	Stewed without sugar	Stems and juice	96	95·9	1·8	0·7	0·0	0·07
341	Strawberries	Raw..	Flesh and pips, no stalks	97	88·9	2·2	6·2	0·0	0·10
342	Sultanas, dried	Raw..	Whole fruit	100	18·3	7·0	64·7	0·0	0·28
343	Tangerines	Raw..	Flesh only, no peel or pips	70	86·7	1·9	8·0	0·0	0·14
343*a*	Tangerines (weighed with peel and pips)	Raw..	Flesh only, no peel or pips	70	60·6	1·3	5·6	0·0	0·10

No.	Food.	g. per 100 g.			Calories per 100 g.	mg. per 100 g.									Acid-base balance, c.c. per 100 g.	
		Protein (N × 6·25).	Fat.	Available carbohydrate (as monosaccharides).		Na.	K.	Ca.	Mg.	Fe.	Cu.	P.	S.	Cl.	$\frac{N}{10}$ Acid.	$\frac{N}{10}$ Alkali.
327	Pineapple, fresh.. ..	0·5	Tr.	11·6	46	1·6	247	12·2	16·9	0·42	0·08	7·8	2·6	28·5		70
328	Pineapple, tinned in syrup	0·3	Tr.	16·5	63	0·5	57	13·4	8·1	1·70	0·05	5·0	2·7	4·2		22
329	Plums, Victoria dessert	0·6	Tr.	9·6	38	1·7	188	11·0	7·2	0·36	0·10	16·3	3·5	$<$1·0		48
329*a*	Plums, Victoria dessert (weighed with stones)	0·6	Tr.	9·0	36	1·6	177	10·4	6·8	0·34	0·09	15·3	3·3	$<$1·0		45
330	Plums, cooking, raw ..	0·6	Tr.	6·2	26	2·0	195	13·7	7·9	0·30	0·09	14·5	4·6	$<$1·0		52
330*a*	Plums, cooking, raw (weighed with stones)	0·5	Tr.	5·6	23	1·8	177	12·5	7·2	0·27	0·08	13·2	4·2	$<$1·0		47
331	Plums, stewed without sugar (weighed with stones)	0·4	Tr.	4·0	17	1·3	126	8·9	5·1	0·19	0·06	9·4	3·0	$<$1·0		34
332	Pomegranate juice ..	0·2	Tr.	11·6	44	1·1	204	2·9	3·1	0·15	0·07	7·5	4·2	52·5		35
333	Prunes, dried, raw ..	2·4	Tr.	40·3	161	12·2	864	37·7	26·7	2·90	0·16	83·0	18·5	2·5		203
333*a*	Prunes, dried, raw (weighed with stones)	2·0	Tr.	33·5	134	10·2	718	31·3	22·2	2·41	0·13	69·0	15·4	2·1		169
334	Prunes, stewed without sugar (weighed with stones)	0·9	Tr.	15·5	62	4·7	333	14·5	10·3	1·12	0·06	32·0	7·1	1·0		78
335	Quinces	0·3	Tr.	6·3	25	3·2	203	13·9	6·0	0·32	0·13	19·0	5·2	1·9		49
336	Raisins, dried	1·1	Tr.	64·4	247	52·2	860	60·6	41·7	1·55	0·24	32·8	23·0	8·5		270
337	Raspberries, raw ..	0·9	Tr.	5·6	25	2·5	224	40·7	21·6	1·21	0·21	28·7	17·3	22·3		61
338	Raspberries, stewed without sugar	0·6	Tr.	3·8	17	1·7	152	27·6	14·6	0·82	0·14	19·5	11·7	15·1		41
339	Rhubarb, raw	0·6	Tr.	1·0	6	2·2	425	103·0	13·6	0·40	0·13	21·0	8·2	87·0		130
340	Rhubarb, stewed without sugar	0·4	Tr.	0·7	4	1·5	297	72·0	9·5	0·28	0·09	14·7	5·7	60·9		91
341	Strawberries	0·6	Tr.	6·2	26	1·5	161	22·0	11·7	0·71	0·13	23·0	13·4	17·5		35
342	Sultanas, dried	1·7	Tr.	64·7	249	52·7	856	52·2	35·3	1·82	0·35	94·5	44·3	15·5		204
343	Tangerines	0·9	Tr.	8·0	34	2·2	155	41·5	11·2	0·27	0·09	16·7	10·3	2·4		53
343*a*	Tangerines (weighed with peel and pips)	0·6	Tr.	5·6	24	1·5	108	29·0	7·8	0·19	0·06	11·7	7·2	1·7		37

Nuts

No.	Food.	Nature of edible (analysed) material.	Edible matter, as eaten, expressed as a percentage of the weight as purchased.	Water.	Unavailable carbohydrate.*	Sugar (as invert sugar).	Starch (as glucose).	Total nitrogen.
344	Almonds	Kernel only, no shell ..	37	4·7	14·3	4·3	0·0	3·27
344*a*	Almonds (weighed with shells)	Kernel only, no shell ..	37	1·7	5·3	1·6	0·0	1·21
345	Barcelona nuts	Kernel only, no shell ..	62	5·7	10·3	3·4	1·8	2·06
345*a*	Barcelona nuts (weighed with shells) ..	Kernel only, no shell ..	62	3·5	6·4	2·1	1·1	1·28
346	Brazil nuts	Kernel only, no shell ..	45	8·5	9·0	1·7	2·4	2·21
346*a*	Brazil nuts (weighed with shells) ..	Kernel only, no shell ..	45	3·8	4·1	0·8	1·1	0·99
347	Chestnuts	Kernel only, no shell ..	83	51·7	6·8	7·0	29·6	0·37
347*a*	Chestnuts (weighed with shells)	Kernel only, no shell ..	83	42·8	5·7	5·8	24·6	0·31
348	Cob nuts	Kernel only, no shell ..	36	41·1	6·1	4·7	2·1	1·44
348*a*	Cob nuts (weighed with shells)	Kernel only, no shell ..	36	14·8	2·2	1·7	0·8	0·52
349	Coconut, fresh	Kernel only, no shell ..	70	42·0	13·6	3·7	0·0	0·61
350	Coconut milk	Milk only	15	92·2	—	4·9	0·0	0·06
351	Coconut, desiccated	As purchased	100	Tr.	23·5	6·4	0·0	1·05
352	Peanuts	Kernel only, no shell ..	69	4·5	8·1	3·1	5·5	4·50
352*a*	Peanuts (weighed with shells)	Kernel only, no shell ..	69	3·1	5·6	2·1	3·8	3·10
353	Walnuts	Kernel only, no shell ..	64	23·5	5·2	3·2	1·8	2·00
353*a*	Walnuts (weighed with shells)	Kernel only, no shell ..	64	15·0	3·3	2·0	1·2	1·28

* Undetermined matter, probably unavailable carbohydrate.

Nuts—*continued*

No.	Food.	*g. per 100 g.* Protein (N × 6·25).	Fat.	Available carbohydrate (as monosaccharides).	Calories per 100 g.	*mg. per 100 g.* Na.	K.	Ca.	Mg.	Fe.	Cu.	P.	S.	Cl.	*Acid-base balance, c.c. per 100 g.* $\frac{N}{10}$ Acid.	$\frac{N}{10}$ Alkali.
344	Almonds	20·5	53·5	4·3	598	5·8	856	247	257	4·23	0·14	442	145	1·7		183
344a	Almonds (weighed with shells)	7·6	19·8	1·6	221	2·1	316	92	95	1·56	0·05	164	54	0·6		68
345	Barcelona nuts	12·9	64·0	5·2	667	2·5	935	170	202	2·97	0·96	299	176	33·5		182
345a	Barcelona nuts (weighed with shells)	8·0	39·6	3·2	413	1·6	580	106	125	1·84	0·60	185	109	20·8		113
346	Brazil nuts	13·8	61·5	4·1	644	1·5	760	176	411	2·82	1·10	592	293	61·0		45
346a	Brazil nuts (weighed with shells)	6·2	27·6	1·8	289	0·7	342	79	185	1·27	0·50	267	132	27·4		20
347	Chestnuts	2·3	2·7	36·6	172	10·9	497	46	33	0·89	0·23	74	29	15·0		113
347a	Chestnuts (weighed with shells)	1·9	2·2	30·4	142	9·1	412	38	27	0·74	0·19	61	24	12·4		94
348	Cob nuts	9·0	36·0	6·8	398	1·4	345	44	56	1·06	0·21	229	75	5·9	39	
348a	Cob nuts (weighed with shells)	3·2	13·0	2·4	143	0·5	124	16	20	0·38	0·08	82	27	2·1	14	
349	Coconut, fresh	3·8	36·0	3·7	365	16·5	436	13	52	2·08	0·32	94	44	114·0		49
350	Coconut milk	0·4	—	4·9	—	105·0	312	29	30	0·10	0·04	37	24	183·0		75
351	Coconut desiccated ..	6·6	62·0	6·4	628	28·4	751	22	90	3·59	0·55	162	76	196·0		85
352	Peanuts	28·1	49·0	8·6	603	5·6	680	61	181	2·04	0·27	365	377	6·8	116	
352a	Peanuts (weighed with shells)	19·4	33·8	5·9	416	3·9	469	42	125	1·41	0·19	252	260	4·7	80	
353	Walnuts	12·5	51·5	5·0	549	2·7	687	61	131	2·35	0·31	510	104	23·0	84	
353a	Walnuts (weighed with shells)	8·0	33·0	3·2	352	1·7	439	39	84	1·50	0·20	326	67	14·7	54	

Vegetables

No.	Food.	Method and time of cooking.	Nature of edible (analysed) material.	Edible matter, as eaten, expressed as a percentage of the weight as purchased.	g. per 100 g.				
					Water.	Unavailable carbohydrate.	Sugar (as invert sugar).	Starch (as glucose).	Total nitrogen.
354	Artichokes, globe	Boiled 35 minutes ..	Base of leaves and soft inside parts	41	84·4	—	—	0·0	0·18
354a	Artichokes, globe (weighed as served)	Boiled 35 minutes ..	Base of leaves and soft inside parts	41	36·3	—	—	0·0	0·08
355	Artichokes, Jerusalem ..	Boiled 20 minutes ..	Flesh only	85	80·2	—	—	0·0	0·25
356	Asparagus	Boiled 25 minutes ..	Soft tips	20	92·4	1·5	1·1	0·0	0·54
356a	Asparagus (weighed as served)	Boiled 25 minutes ..	Soft tips	20	46·2	0·8	0·6	0·0	0·27
357	Beans, baked	Tinned	Contents of tin as purchased	100	69·6	5·1	6·1	11·2	0·96
358	Beans, broad	Boiled 30 minutes ..	Whole beans, without pods	31	83·7	4·2	0·6	6·5	0·66
359	Beans, butter	Raw	Whole beans	100	8·7	24·5	3·6	46·2	3·06
360	Beans, butter	Soaked 24 hours, boiled 2 hours	Whole beans	250	70·5	5·1	1·5	15·6	1·13
361	Beans, French	Cut up and boiled 30 minutes	Flesh and skin of pods and beans	100	95·5	3·2	0·8	0·3	0·12
362	Beans, haricot	Raw	Whole beans	100	7·9	28·8	2·8	42·7	3·42
363	Beans, haricot	Soaked 24 hours, boiled 2 hours	Whole beans	260	69·6	7·4	0·8	15·8	1·06
364	Beans, runner	Raw	Flesh and skin of pods and beans	86	91·6	3·0	2·7	0·2	0·18
365	Beans, runner	Cut up and boiled 25 minutes	Flesh and skin of pods and beans	86	93·6	3·0	0·8	0·1	0·12
366	Beetroot*	Boiled 2 hours	Flesh only, no skin ..	80	82·7	2·5	9·9	0·0	0·29

* Weighed cold.

Vegetables—*continued*

No.	Food.	Protein (N × 6·25). g. per 100 g.	Fat. g. per 100 g.	Available carbohydrate (as monosaccharides). g. per 100 g.	Calories per 100 g.	Na. mg. per 100 g.	K.	Ca.	Mg.	Fe.	Cu.	P.	S.	Cl.	$\frac{N}{10}$ Acid. Acid-base balance, c.c per 100 g.	$\frac{N}{10}$ Alkali.
354	Artichokes, globe, boiled	1·1	Tr.	*2·7	15	14·8	327	43·5	27·2	0·49	0·09	39·7	15·5	83·5		76
354a	Artichokes, globe, boiled (weighed as served)	0·5	Tr.	*1·2	7	6·4	141	18·7	11·7	0·21	0·04	17·1	6·7	35·9		33
355	Artichokes, Jerusalem, boiled	1·6	Tr.	*3·2	19	2·6	420	30·3	11·4	0·41	0·12	33·0	21·6	57·5		82
356	Asparagus, boiled ..	3·4	Tr.	1·1	18	1·7	235	25·8	10·4	0·89	0·20	84·5	46·6	31·4	10	
356a	Asparagus, boiled (weighed as served)	1·7	Tr.	0·6	9	0·9	118	12·9	5·2	0·45	0·10	42·3	23·3	15·7	5	
357	Beans, baked	6·0	0·4	17·3	93	(591)	344	61·6	36·7	2·05	0·24	184·0	50·7	(810)		28
358	Beans, broad, boiled ..	4·1	Tr.	7·1	43	19·6	233	21·2	27·6	0·98	0·43	99·0	27·0	14·2		17
359	Beans, butter, raw ..	19·2	Tr.	49·8	266	61·5	1700	84·8	164·0	5·92	1·22	318·0	109·0	46·5		355
360	Beans, butter, boiled ..	7·1	Tr.	17·1	93	16·2	398	18·7	33·3	1·67	0·16	86·5	47·2	2·4		60
361	Beans, French, boiled ..	0·8	Tr.	1·1	7	3·4	102	38·6	10·1	0·59	0·10	15·2	8·3	10·7		37
362	Beans, haricot, raw ..	21·4	Tr.	45·5	258	43·2	1160	180·0	183·0	6·65	0·61	309·0	166·0	1·8		255
363	Beans, haricot, boiled ..	6·6	Tr.	16·6	89	15·0	320	64·5	44·5	2·50	0·14	122·0	46·3	1·1		50
364	Beans, runner, raw ..	1·1	Tr.	2·9	15	6·5	276	33·3	23·0	0·74	0·09	25·9	14·1	22·7		77
365	Beans, runner, boiled ..	0·8	Tr.	0·9	7	3·3	87	25·6	12·5	0·59	0·03	10·7	9·5	8·8		32
366	Beetroot, boiled.. ..	1·8	Tr.	9·9	44	64·0	350	30·0	16·9	0·70	0·14	35·6	22·1	75·5		89

* This vegetable contains inulin. 50 per cent. total carbohydrate taken to be available.

Vegetables—*continued*

No.	Food.	Method and time of cooking.	Nature of edible (analysed) material.	Edible matter, as eaten, expressed as a percentage of the weight as purchased.	g. per 100 g. Water.	Unavailable carbohydrate.	Sugar (as invert sugar).	Starch (as glucose).	Total nitrogen.
367	Broccoli tops	Boiled 45 minutes	Leaves only, no thick stem	42	90·8	4·2	0·4	0·0	0·50
368	Brussels sprouts	Boiled 30 minutes	Inner leaves	94	90·8	4·8	1·1	0·6	0·38
369	Cabbage, red	Raw	Inner leaves	70	89·7	3·4	3·5	0·0	0·27
370	Cabbage, Savoy	Raw	Inner leaves	53	89·9	3·1	3·3	0·0	0·53
371	Cabbage, Savoy	Boiled 30 minutes	Inner leaves	65	95·7	2·5	1·1	0·0	0·21
372	Cabbage, spring	Boiled 30 minutes	Inner leaves	59	96·6	2·2	0·8	0·0	0·18
373	Cabbage, winter	Raw	Inner leaves	60	90·6	2·5	8·3	0·0	0·43
374	Cabbage, winter	Boiled 45 minutes	Inner leaves	71	95·9	2·5	1·2	0·1	0·13
375	Carrageen moss	Dried	Whole moss	100	13·9	71·3	0·4	0·0	1·08
376	Carrots, old	Raw	Flesh only	96	89·8	2·9	5·4	0·0	0·11
377	Carrots, old	Boiled 45 minutes	Flesh only	87	91·5	3·1	4·2	0·1	0·10
378	Carrots, young	Boiled 25 minutes	Flesh only	50	81·1	3·0	4·4	0·1	0·14
379	Cauliflower	Boiled 30 minutes	Flower and inner leaves	42	94·9	2·4	1·2	0·0	0·24
380	Celeriac	Boiled 30 minutes	Flesh only	79	90·2	4·9	1·5	0·5	0·26
381	Celery	Raw	Stem only	73	93·5	1·8	1·2	0·1	0·15
382	Celery	Boiled 30 minutes	Stem only	72	95·7	2·2	0·7	0·0	0·10
383	Chicory	Raw	Stem and young leaves	79	96·2	—	—	0·0	0·12
384	Cucumber	Raw	Flesh only	77	96·4	0·4	1·8	0·0	0·10
385	Egg plant	Raw	Flesh only	77	93·4	2·5	2·9	0·2	0·11
386	Endive	Raw	Leaves only	63	93·7	2·2	1·0	0·0	0·28
387	Horseradish	Raw	Flesh of root	45	74·7	8·3	7·3	3·7	0·72
388	Leeks	Boiled 30 minutes	Bulb only	44	90·8	3·9	4·6	0·0	0·28
389	Lentils	Raw	Lentils as purchased	100	6·5	17·4	2·4	50·8	3·80
390	Lentils	Soaked 24 hours, boiled 2 hours.	Lentils as purchased	290	71·9	2·4	0·9	17·4	1·08

Vegetables—*continued*

No.	Food.	g. per 100 g. Protein (N × 6·25).	Fat.	Available carbohydrate (as monosaccharides).	Calories per 100 g.	mg. per 100 g. Na.	K.	Ca.	Mg.	Fe.	Cu.	P.	S.	Cl.	Acid-base balance, c.c. per 100 g. N/10 Acid.	N/10 Alkali.
367	Broccoli tops, boiled ..	3·1	Tr.	0·4	14	6·8	103	160·0	13·5	1·52	0·10	54·0	45·0	51·2		43
368	Brussels sprouts, boiled	2·4	Tr.	1·7	16	7·7	247	27·1	10·6	0·63	0·08	44·8	77·8	11·4		8
369	Cabbage, red, raw ..	1·7	Tr.	3·5	20	31·6	302	53·2	16·5	0·57	0·09	32·1	68·0	44·5		56
370	Cabbage, Savoy, raw ..	3·3	Tr.	3·3	26	22·5	263	75·0	19·5	0·90	—	67·7	88·0	22·3		26
371	Cabbage, Savoy, boiled ..	1·3	Tr.	1·1	9	8·1	122	52·5	7·2	0·72	0·07	27·2	30·4	9·4		28
372	Cabbage, spring, boiled ..	1·1	Tr.	0·8	8	12·3	108	30·0	6·3	0·45	0·07	31·8	26·7	6·4		14
373	Cabbage, winter, raw ..	2·7	Tr.	8·3	42	28·4	240	72·3	16·8	1·23	—	64·1	71·8	39·6		27
374	Cabbage, winter, boiled ..	0·8	Tr.	1·3	8	13·5	144	58·2	7·3	0·47	0·04	16·2	23·4	13·7		49
375	Carrageen moss, dried ..	6·8	Tr.	0·4	29	2890·0	2100	845·0	630·0	8·88	0·51	205·0	5460·0	1150·0	1130	
376	Carrots, old, raw ..	0·7	Tr.	5·4	23	95·0	224	48·0	12·0	0·56	0·08	21·0	6·9	68·5		90
377	Carrots, old, boiled ..	0·6	Tr.	4·3	19	50·0	87	36·9	6·4	0·37	0·08	16·7	5·0	31·1		44
378	Carrots, young, boiled ..	0·9	Tr.	4·5	21	22·5	237	28·8	8·4	0·43	0·08	29·5	9·3	27·5		59
379	Cauliflower, boiled ..	1·5	Tr.	1·2	11	11·4	152	23·0	6·6	0·48	0·06	33·0	29·4	11·6		17
380	Celeriac, boiled	1·6	Tr.	2·0	14	28·2	400	46·5	12·0	0·84	0·13	71·0	12·8	23·4		88
381	Celery, raw	0·9	Tr.	1·3	9	137·0	278	52·2	9·6	0·61	0·11	31·7	14·9	183·0		84
382	Celery, boiled	0·6	Tr.	0·7	5	66·5	132	52·0	8·6	0·43	0·11	19·3	8·3	100·0		50
383	Chicory, raw	0·8	Tr.	*1·5	9	7·3	182	18·4	12·6	0·69	0·14	20·9	12·7	25·0		41
384	Cucumber, raw	0·6	Tr.	1·8	9	13·0	141	22·8	9·1	0·30	0·09	24·1	11·0	24·5		32
385	Egg plant, raw	0·7	Tr.	3·1	15	2·5	238	10·4	9·5	0·39	0·08	12·1	9·0	61·0		45
386	Endive, raw	1·8	Tr.	1·0	11	10·1	381	43·9	10·4	2·77	0·09	66·5	25·7	70·5		54
387	Horseradish, raw ..	4·5	Tr.	11·0	60	7·9	579	119·0	35·8	2·03	0·14	70·0	212·0	18·8		58
388	Leeks, boiled	1·8	Tr.	4·6	25	6·4	278	60·5	12·5	2·00	0·09	27·5	48·9	42·6		55
389	Lentils, raw	23·8	Tr.	53·2	297	36·0	673	38·6	76·5	7·62	0·58	242·0	122·0	63·5		20
390	Lentils, boiled	6·8	Tr.	18·3	96	9·4	217	10·5	20·7	2·20	0·27	80·0	37·3	12·7		4

* This vegetable contains inulin. 50 per cent. total carbohydrate taken to be available.

Vegetables—*continued*

No.	Food.	Method and time of cooking.	Nature of edible (analysed) material.	Edible matter, as eaten, expressed as a percentage of the weight as purchased.	g. per 100 g. Water.	Unavailable carbohydrate.	Sugar (as invert sugar).	Starch (as glucose).	Total nitrogen.
391	Lettuce	Raw	Inner leaves of long and headed forms	45	95·2	1·4	1·8	0·0	0·17
392	Marrow	Boiled 25 minutes ..	Flesh only	64	97·8	0·6	1·3	0·1	0·06
393	Mushrooms	Raw	Flesh and stem	75	91·5	2·5	0·0	0·0	0·74*
394	Mushrooms	Fried in dripping ..	Flesh and stem	61	64·2	—	0·0	0·0	0·90*
395	Mustard and cress ..	Raw	Leaves and stems ..	100	92·5	3·7	0·9	0·0	0·26
396	Onions	Raw	Flesh only	97	92·8	1·3	5·2	0·0	0·15
397	Onions	Boiled 30 minutes ..	Flesh only	85	96·6	1·3	2·7	0·0	0·09
398	Onions	Cut up and fried in dripping	Flesh only	49	42·0	—	10·1	0·0	0·90
399	Onions, spring	Raw	Flesh of bulb	31	86·8	3·1	8·5	0·0	0·15
400	Parsley	Raw	Leaves	53	78·7	9·1	Tr.	0·0	0·83
401	Parsnips	Raw	Flesh only	74	82·5	4·0	8·8	2·5	0·27
402	Parsnips	Boiled 30 minutes ..	Flesh only	78	83·2	2·5	2·7	10·8	0·20
403	Peas, fresh	Raw	Whole peas, no pods ..	37	78·5	5·2	4·0	6·6	0·92
404	Peas, fresh	Boiled 20 minutes ..	Whole peas, no pods ..	37	80·0	5·2	1·8	5·9	0·80
405	Peas, dried	Raw	Whole peas	100	8·7	21·3	2·4	47·6	3·45
406	Peas, dried	Soaked 24 hours, boiled 2 hours	Whole peas	270	70·3	4·8	0·9	18·2	1·11
407	Peas, split, dried ..	Raw	Peas as purchased ..	100	6·8	17·2	1·9	54·7	3·54
408	Peas, split, dried ..	Soaked 24 hours, boiled 2 hours	Peas as purchased ..	250	67·3	5·1	0·9	21·0	1·33
409	Peas	Tinned	Whole peas	100	72·7	4·4	2·3	14·2	0·94
410	Potatoes, old	Raw	Flesh only	86	75·8	2·1	0·5	20·3	0·34
411	Potatoes, old, peel ..	Raw	Peel only	—	80·0	2·6	0·4	15·5	0·40

* 60 per cent. of this nitrogen is present as urea.

Vegetables—*continued*

No	Food.	g. per 100 g. Protein (N × 6·25).	Fat.	Available carbohydrate (as monosaccharides).	Calories per 100 g.	mg. per 100 g. Na.	K.	Ca.	Mg.	Fe.	Cu.	P.	S.	Cl.	Acid-base balance, c.c. per 100 g. $\frac{N}{10}$ Acid.	$\frac{N}{10}$ Alkali.
391	Lettuce, raw	1·1	Tr.	1·8	11	3·1	208	25·9	9·7	0·73	0·15	30·2	11·8	39·5		38
392	Marrow, boiled	0·4	Tr.	1·4	7	1·2	84	13·6	6·7	0·22	0·03	12·7	5·5	13·9		19
393	Mushrooms, raw	*1·8	Tr.	0·0	7	9·1	467	2·9	13·2	1·03	0·64	136·0	33·8	84·5		4
394	Mushrooms, fried	*2·2	22·3	0·0	217	11·0	568	3·5	16·0	1·25	0·78	166·0	73·8	103·0	16	
395	Mustard and cress, raw	1·6	Tr.	0·9	10	19·0	337	65·9	27·3	4·54	0·12	65·5	170·0	89·0	23	
396	Onions, raw	0·9	Tr.	5·2	23	10·2	137	31·2	7·6	0·30	0·08	30·0	50·7	19·5		5
397	Onions, boiled	0·6	Tr.	2·7	13	6·6	78	24·4	4·9	0·25	0·07	16·4	23·7	4·9		2
398	Onions, fried	1·8	33·3	10·1	355	20·0	267	61·0	14·8	0·59	0·16	59·0	87·8	38·0		16
399	Onions, spring, raw	0·9	Tr.	8·5	36	13·0	226	135·0	10·9	1·24	0·13	23·6	50·0	35·5		84
400	Parsley, raw	5·2	Tr.	Tr.	21	33·0	1080	325·0	52·2	8·00	0·52	128·0	—	156·0	—	—
401	Parsnips, raw	1·7	Tr.	11·3	49	16·5	342	54·8	22·4	0·57	0·10	69·0	16·5	40·5		75
402	Parsnips, boiled	1·3	Tr.	13·5	56	4·1	293	35·5	13·0	0·45	0·10	31·7	14·6	32·7		67
403	Peas, fresh, raw	5·8	Tr.	10·6	64	0·5	342	15·1	30·2	1·88	0·23	104·0	50·0	38·0		12
404	Peas, fresh, boiled	5·0	Tr.	7·7	49	Tr.	174	12·6	21·4	1·22	0·15	83·3	43·5	7·8	14	
405	Peas, dried, raw	21·5	Tr.	50·0	275	37·9	985	60·8	116·0	4·73	0·49	303·0	129·0	60·0		103
406	Peas, dried, boiled	6·9	Tr.	19·1	100	12·6	267	24·4	30·3	1·44	0·17	113·0	39·0	9·3		12
407	Peas, split, dried, raw	22·1	Tr.	56·6	303	38·3	910	33·0	125·0	5·40	0·58	268·0	166·0	56·0		77
408	Peas, split, dried, boiled	8·3	Tr.	21·9	116	14·2	269	10·8	30·2	1·74	0·25	122·0	45·7	10·2	5	
409	Peas, tinned	5·9	Tr.	16·5	86	(260)	201	25·7	24·4	1·87	0·21	169·0	43·9	(318)	29	
410	Potatoes, old, raw	2·1	Tr.	20·8	87	6·5	568	7·7	24·2	0·75	0·15	40·3	34·6	78·5		103
411	Potatoes, old, raw, peel	2·5	Tr.	15·9	70	7·0	650	27·0	27·6	2·00	0·25	36·4	—	95·0	—	—

* *See* page 6.

Vegetables—*continued*

No.	Food.	Method and time of cooking.	Nature of edible (analysed) material.	Edible matter, as eaten, expressed as a percentage of the weight as purchased.	g. per 100 g.				
					Water.	Unavailable carbohydrate.	Sugar (as invert sugar).	Starch (as glucose).	Total nitrogen.
412	Potatoes, old	Boiled 30 minutes	Flesh only (peeled before boiling)	86	80·5	1·0	0·4	19·3	0·23
413	Potatoes, old	Boiled and mashed with margarine and milk	Flesh only	94	76·9	0·9	0·6	17·4	0·24
414	Potatoes, old	Baked in skins	Flesh only	68	71·0	2·5	0·6	24·4	0·41
414*a*	Potatoes, old (weighed with skin)	Baked in skins	Flesh only	68	57·5	2·0	0·5	19·8	0·33
415	Potatoes, old	Roast in shallow fat	Flesh only	66	64·3	—	—	—	0·45
416	Potatoes, old, "chips"	Cut in cubes and fried in deep fat	Flesh only	49	47·0	—	—	—	0·61
417	Potatoes, new	Boiled 15 minutes	Flesh only	96	78·8	2·0	0·7	17·6	0·25
418	Pumpkin	Raw	Flesh only	81	94·7	0·5	2·7	0·7	0·10
419	Radishes	Raw	Flesh and skin	50	93·3	1·0	2·8	0·0	0·16
420	Salsify	Boiled 45 minutes	Flesh only	63	81·2	—	—	0·0	0·30
421	Seakale	Boiled 20 minutes	Stem only	74	95·6	1·2	0·6	0·0	0·23
422	Spinach	Boiled 15 minutes, without added water	Leaves	42	85·1	6·3	1·2	0·2	0·81
423	Spring greens	Boiled 30 minutes	Leaves	100	93·6	3·8	0·9	0·0	0·27
424	Swedes	Raw	Flesh only	86	91·4	2·7	4·2	0·1	0·18
425	Swedes	Boiled 45 minutes	Flesh only	82	91·6	2·8	3·7	0·1	0·14
426	Sweet potatoes	Boiled 30 minutes	Flesh only	88	72·0	2·3	9·1	11·0	0·17
427	Tomatoes	Raw	Flesh, skin and seeds	100	93·4	1·5	2·8	Tr.	0·14
428	Tomatoes	Fried in dripping	Flesh, skin and seeds	87	86·5	—	3·3	Tr.	0·16
429	Turnips	Raw	Flesh only	84	93·3	2·8	3·8	0·0	0·12
430	Turnips	Boiled 30 minutes	Flesh only	80	94·5	2·2	2·3	0·0	0·11
431	Turnip tops	Boiled 20 minutes	Leaves	45	92·8	3·9	0·0	0·1	0·43
432	Watercress	Raw	Leaves and part of stem	77	91·1	3·3	0·6	0·1	0·46

Vegetables—*continued*

No.	Food.	g. per 100 g. Protein (N × 6·25).	Fat.	Available carbohydrate (as monosaccharides).	Calories per 100 g.	mg. per 100 g. Na.	K.	Ca.	Mg.	Fe.	Cu.	P.	S.	Cl.	Acid-base balance, c.c. per 100 g. $\frac{N}{10}$ Acid.	$\frac{N}{10}$ Alkali.
412	Potatoes, old, boiled ..	1·4	Tr.	19·7	80	3·4	325	4·3	15·0	0·48	0·11	29·0	22·2	40·7		53
413	Potatoes, old, mashed ..	1·5	5·0	18·0	120	(24)	302	11·7	14·4	0·45	0·10	31·6	23·5	(71)		51
414	Potatoes, old, baked in skins	2·5	Tr.	25·0	104	7·8	680	9·2	29·0	0·90	0·18	48·3	41·5	94·0		124
414*a*	Potatoes, old, baked in skins (weighed with skins)	2·0	Tr.	20·3	84	6·3	550	7·5	23·5	0·73	0·15	39·1	33·6	76·1		100
415	Potatoes, old, roast ..	2·8	1·0	27·3	123	8·6	745	10·1	32·0	0·99	0·20	53·0	56·3	103·0		128
416	Potatoes, old, "chips" ..	3·8	9·0	37·3	239	11·7	1020	13·8	43·3	1·35	0·27	72·2	44·7	140·0		196
417	Potatoes, new, boiled ..	1·6	Tr.	18·3	75	40·5	330	5·0	19·6	0·46	0·15	33·0	24·3	45·5		72
418	Pumpkin, raw	0·6	Tr.	3·4	15	1·3	309	39·0	8·2	0·39	0·08	19·4	9·5	36·5		78
419	Radishes, raw	1·0	Tr.	2·8	15	59·0	240	43·7	11·4	1·88	0·13	27·1	37·5	18·8		72
420	Salsify, boiled	1·9	Tr.	*2·8	18	8·4	183	60·0	14·2	1·23	0·12	53·0	25·2	46·0		29
421	Seakale, boiled	1·4	Tr.	0·6	8	3·9	50	47·8	10·5	0·60	0·07	33·5	52·0	12·4	10	
422	Spinach, boiled	5·1	Tr.	1·4	26	123·0	490	595·0	59·2	4·00	0·26	93·0	86·5	55·5		396
423	Spring greens, boiled ..	1·7	Tr.	0·9	10	10·3	118	86·0	8·6	1·33	0·08	30·5	28·5	16·1		43
424	Swedes, raw	1·1	Tr.	4·3	21	52·2	136	56·4	10·8	0·35	0·05	19·0	39·1	30·5		49
425	Swedes, boiled	0·9	Tr.	3·8	18	14·4	102	41·5	7·0	0·29	0·04	18·4	30·5	9·3		26
426	Sweet potatoes, boiled ..	1·1	Tr.	20·1	80	17·8	296	20·5	12·3	0·62	0·15	43·5	14·9	60·0		50
427	Tomatoes, raw	0·9	Tr.	2·8	14	2·8	288	13·3	11·0	0·43	0·10	21·3	10·7	51·0		56
428	Tomatoes, fried	1·0	5·9	3·3	71	3·3	335	15·4	12·8	0·50	0·12	24·8	9·2	59·0		68
429	Turnips, raw	0·8	Tr.	3·8	18	58·0	238	58·8	7·4	0·37	0·07	27·5	22·1	70·0		65
430	Turnips, boiled	0·7	Tr.	2·3	11	28·3	160	55·0	6·6	0·35	0·04	19·2	21·2	31·4		52
431	Turnip tops, boiled ..	2·7	Tr.	0·1	11	6·7	78	98·0	10·1	3·08	0·09	45·1	39·0	14·8		23
432	Watercress, raw.. ..	2·9	Tr.	0·7	15	60·0	314	222·0	17·0	1·62	0·14	52·0	127·0	156·0		75

* This vegetable contains inulin. 50 per cent. total carbohydrate taken to be available

Sugar, Preserves and Sweetmeats

No.	Food.	Description and number of samples.	g. per 100 g.			
			Water.	Sugar (as invert sugar).	Starch and dextrins (as glucose).	Total nitrogen.
433	Blackcurrant purée	Mixed sample supplied by the makers	57·0	40·0	0·0	0·07
434	Cherries, glacé	3 samples from different shops	—	55·8	0·0	0·10
435	Chocolate, blended (1943)	3 well-known varieties	Tr.	51·5	0·7	1·47
436	Chocolate, milk (1935)	5 well-known varieties	1·3	42·3	10·0	1·19
437	Chocolate, milk (1943)	2 well-known varieties	Tr.	53·8	0·7	1·39
438	Chocolate, plain (1935)	5 well-known varieties	Tr.	52·6	6·1	0·74
439	Chocolate, plain (1943)	4 well-known varieties	Tr.	49·8	2·7	0·89
440	Chutney, apple	Recipe p. 10	45·0	51·9	0·4	0·13
441	Chutney, tomato	Recipe p. 11	58·2	38·5	0·3	0·18
442	Comb honey	2 samples from different shops	20·2	74·4	0·0	0·09
443	Honey, in jars	2 samples from different shops	23·0	76·4	0·0	0·06
444	Ice cream	3 varieties of ice cream bricks	62·8	17·5	0·0	0·63
445	Jam, fruit with edible seeds	Blackberry, blackcurrant, gooseberry, raspberry, strawberry. Two samples of each, different makers	29·8	69·0	0·0	0·10
446	Jam, stone fruit	Apricot, damson, greengage, plum. Two samples of each, different makers	29·6	69·3	0·0	0·06
447	Jelly, packet	8 samples, assorted flavours	29·9	62·5	0·0	1·10
448	Lemon curd	Recipe p. 11	42·1	42·5	0·0	0·52
449	Marmalade	4 varieties	28·0	69·5	0·0	0·01
450	Mincemeat	2 varieties	69·3	25·5	0·0	0·09
451	Sugar, Demerara	5 samples from different shops	Tr.	*99·3	0·0	0·08
452	Sugar, white	Granulated and loaf	Tr.	*99·9	0·0	Tr.
453	Syrup, golden	3 samples of well-known brand	20·0	79·0	0·0	0·05
454	Toffee, home-made	Recipe p. 11	5·5	90·8	0·0	0·03
455	Treacle, black	3 samples from different shops	28·5	67·2	0·0	0·19

* As sucrose.

Sugar, Preserves and Sweetmeats—*continued*

No.	Food.	g. per 100 g. Protein (N × 6·25).	Fat.	Available carbohydrate (as monosaccharides).	Calories per 100 g.	mg. per 100 g. Na.	K.	Ca.	Mg.	Fe.	Cu.	P.	S.	Cl.	Acid-base balance, c.c. per 100 g. N/10 Acid.	N/10 Alkali.
433	Blackcurrant purée ..	0·4	Tr.	40·0	152	11·0	200	34·0	11·8	1·60	0·15	25·0	32·0	13·0		43
434	Cherries, glacé	0·6	0·0	55·8	212	64·8	18	44·3	8·2	2·90	1·28	18·0	21·0	71·0		17
435	Chocolate, blended (1943)	9·2	36·0	52·2	566	(276)	386	253·0	66·4	2·05	0·48	226·0	—	183·0	—	—
436	Chocolate, milk (1935) ..	7·4	34·1	52·3	543	93·4	487	175·0	57·4	1·67	0·14	215·0	67·0	132·0		84
437	Chocolate, milk (1943) ..	8·7	37·6	54·5	588	(275)	349	246·0	58·9	1·71	0·49	218·0	—	170·0	—	—
438	Chocolate, plain (1935) ..	4·6	32·5	58·7	541	18·6	397	26·1	81·7	3·28	1·11	139·0	32·0	8·8		79
439	Chocolate, plain (1943) ..	5·6	35·2	52·5	544	(143)	257	63·0	131·0	2·90	0·81	138·0	—	4·8	—	—
440	Chutney, apple	0·8	0·1	52·3	201	(170)	217	27·4	17·8	1·01	0·10	33·7	32·0	(251)		46
441	Chutney, tomato ..	1·1	0·1	38·8	151	(130)	278	26·2	17·8	0·93	0·12	36·5	31·1	(215)		53
442	Comb honey	0·6	*4·6	74·4	281	7·1	35	7·7	2·0	0·20	0·04	32·3	0·8	26·3	11	
443	Honey, in jars	0·4	Tr.	76·4	288	10·9	51	5·3	2·2	0·39	0·05	17·0	0·8	17·9		6
444	Ice cream	3·9	13·2	17·5	205	64·0	180	152·0	15·3	0·21	0·03	95·5	30·6	103·0		53
445	Jam, fruit with edible seeds.	0·6	0·0	69·0	261	15·9	112	24·2	10·1	1·47	0·23	17·9	6·5	9·2		38
446	Jam, stone fruit ..	0·4	0·0	69·3	261	12·2	104	12·0	5·4	1·02	0·12	18·2	3·2	3·5		28
447	Jelly, packet	†6·1	0·0	62·5	259	25·2	25	31·5	4·4	1·74	0·16	7·0	36·6	30·0		1
448	Lemon curd	3·3	13·9	42·5	302	(63)	67	18·3	5·0	0·72	0·05	62·5	47·0	(84)	35	
449	Marmalade	0·1	0·0	69·5	261	18·2	44	34·7	3·7	0·58	0·12	12·5	2·1	7·1		28
450	Mincemeat	0·6	3·3	25·5	129	(208)	560	52·6	20·8	2·12	0·08	15·7	28·4	(454)		122
451	Sugar, Demerara ..	0·5	0·0	‡104·5	394	6·2	89	52·6	14·8	0·89	0·06	19·9	14·0	35·2		33
452	Sugar, white	Tr.	0·0	‡105·0	394	0·4	2	1·5	0·2	0·04	0·02	Tr.	Tr.	Tr.		<1
453	Syrup, golden	0·3	0·0	79·0	297	270·0	242	26·4	9·5	1·45	0·09	20·0	53·8	41·5		142
454	Toffee, home-made ..	0·2	6·2	90·8	399	(115)	91	11·0	4·0	0·55	0·04	9·7	20·7	(40)		52
455	Treacle, black	1·2	0·0	67·2	257	96·0	1470	495·0	144·0	9·17	0·43	30·6	68·5	815·0		494

* Waxy material, probably not available as fat. Disregarded in calculating calories. † *See* p. 6. ‡ *See* p. 6.

Beverages

No.	Food.	Description and number of samples.	g. per 100 g.				
			Water.	Sugar (as invert sugar).	Starch and dextrins (as glucose).	Total nitrogen.	Purine nitrogen.
456	Bournvita	3 samples from different shops	6·0	60·6	7·0	1·83	—
457	Bovril	3 samples from different shops	—	0·0	0·0	5·95	0·324
458	Cocoa powder	3 varieties	2·5	Tr.	35·0	3·27	—
459	Coffee, ground, roasted	5 samples from different shops	4·1	Tr.	28·5	2·04	0·038
460	Coffee, infusion, 2 minutes	60 g. coffee from mixed sample, boiled in percolator with 900 c.c. water and strained	—	Tr.	0·3	0·03	Tr.
461	Coffee, infusion, 5 minutes	60 g. coffee from mixed sample, boiled in percolator with 900 c.c. water and strained	—	Tr.	0·4	0·04	Tr.
462	Coffee, infusion, 10 minutes	60 g. coffee from mixed sample, boiled in percolator with 900 c.c. water and strained	—	Tr.	0·4	0·05	Tr.
463	Coffee, infusion, 20 minutes	60 g. coffee from mixed sample, boiled in percolator with 900 c.c. water and strained	—	Tr.	0·4	0·05	Tr.
464	Lemonade	Recipe, p. 11	—	12·5	0·0	Tr.	—
465	Malted milk, Horlick's	3 samples from different shops	3·0	50·8	20·0*	2·31	—
466	Marmite	6 samples from different shops	—	0·0	0·0	6·35	0·356
467	Ovaltine	3 samples from different shops	3·3	54·0	7·6*	2·12	—
468	Oxo cubes	3 samples from different shops	—	0·0	0·0	6·93	0·236
469	Tea, Indian	5 samples from different shops	9·3	0·0	0·0	4·08	0·072
470	Tea, Indian, infusion	10 g. tea from mixed sample, infused with 1,000 c.c. boiling water 2–10 minutes and strained	—	0·0	0·0	0·01	Tr.
471	Virol	3 samples from different shops	21·5	62·6	0·0	0·73	—

* Dextrins only.

Beverages—*continued*

No.	Food.	*g. per 100 g. (or 100 c.c.)* Protein.	Fat.	Available carbohydrate (as) monosaccharides).	Calories per 100 g. (or 100c.c.)	*mg. per 100 g. (or 100 c.c.)* Na.	K.	Ca.	Mg.	Fe.	Cu.	P.	S.	Cl.	*Acid-base balance, c.c. per 100 g. (or 100 c.c.)* $\frac{N}{10}$ Acid.	$\frac{N}{10}$ Alkali.
456	Bournvita	11·4	7·5	67·6	370	360·0	660	89·0	170·0	3·3	0·98	411	243	185·0		45
457	Bovril	*29·0	0·7	0·0	125	(5580)	3590	52·0	169·0	12·1	0·83	1300	362	(6880)		510
458	Cocoa powder ..	20·4	25·6	35·0	452	(650)	534	51·2	192·0	14·3	3·40	685	160	199·0		7
459	Coffee, ground, roasted	12·5	15·4	28·5	301	73·5	2020	133·0	235·0	4·1	0·82	161	110	23·6		634
460	Coffee, infusion, 2 min.	0·2	Tr.	0·3	3	0·2	66	2·1	5·5	Tr.	Tr.	1·5	—	0·4	—	—
461	Coffee, infusion, 5 min.	0·3	Tr.	0·4	4	0·3	88	3·4	8·3	Tr.	Tr.	2·8	—	0·6	—	—
462	Coffee, infusion, 10 min.	0·3	Tr.	0·4	5	0·4	104	3·9	10·5	Tr.	Tr.	4·3	—	0·6	—	—
463	Coffee, infusion, 20 min.	0·3	Tr.	0·4	5	0·4	110	4·0	10·8	Tr.	Tr.	4·8	—	0·6	—	—
464	Lemonade	Tr.	Tr.	12·5	47	Tr.	14	0·8	0·7	Tr.	0·01	1·0	Tr.	Tr.		4
465	Malted milk, Horlick's	14·4	8·6	70·8	404	690·0	1128	272·0	71·0	1·3	1·22	402	167	516·0		274
466	Marmite	*10·0	Tr.	0·0	41	(6130)	3440	77·3	276·0	5·2	1·96	1890	382	(7750)		171
467	Ovaltine	13·2	7·9	61·6	356	249·0	1100	339·0	140·0	3·5	0·65	563	183	404·0		85
468	Oxo cubes	*31·9	3·8	0·0	166	(10,600)	2690	101·5	160·0	14·0	0·32	1090	321	(14,000)		635
469	Tea, Indian	14·1	0·0	0·0	58	44·5	2160	426·0	254·0	15·2	1·59	628	177	51·8		465
470	Tea, Indian, infusion..	0·1	0·0	0·0	<1	0·4	17	0·3	1·1	Tr.	Tr.	1·0	—	0·4	—	—
471	Virol	4·6	12·8	59·6	361	(374)	360	108·0	61·5	17·6	0·47	266	83	(596)	30	

* *See* p. 6. Peptides and amino-acids account for most of the non-protein nitrogen in Marmite.

Beers (1938)

No.	Food.	Description and number of samples.	c.c. per 100 c.c.	g. per 100 c.c.	
			Alcohol.	Solids.	Total nitrogen.
472	Mild ale, draught	3 samples, different brewers	4·45	3·3	0·08
473	Mild ale, bottled	3 samples, different brewers	4·74	4·1	0·04
474	Pale ale, draught	4 samples, different brewers	5·95	3·5	0·05
475	Pale ale, bottled	4 samples, different brewers	6·10	3·4	0·04
476	Strong ale	5 samples, different brewers	7·96	5·3	0·08
477	Stout	6 samples, different brewers	4·73	5·0	0·06

Condiments

No.	Food.	Description and number of samples.	g. per 100 g.			
			Water.	Sugar (as invert sugar).	Starch.	Total nitrogen.
478	Curry powder	2 samples from different shops	—*	—	—	1·52
479	Ground ginger	3 samples from different shops	—*	—	—	1·19
480	Mustard	2 varieties	—*	—	—	4·62
481	Pepper	3 samples from different shops	—*	—	—	1·40
482	Salt, block	2 samples from different shops	0·2	0·0	0·0	0·0
483	Table salt "A"†	1 sample	0·1	0·0	0·0	0·0
484	Table salt "B"†	1 sample	0·1	0·0	0·0	0·0
485	Vinegar‡	4 samples from different shops	—	0·6	0·0	0·07

* The loss of weight at 100° C. cannot be used to determine the amount of water present, since these substances contain volatile essential oils.
† The manufacturers of these well known brands of table salt have objected to the composition of their products being published under their trade names.
‡ Contains 4·8 c.c. acetic acid per cent.

(Beers 1938)—*continued*

No.	Food.	*g. per 100 c.c.* Protein (N× 6·25).	Fat.	Available carbohydrate (as monosaccharides).	Calories per 100 g.	*mg. per 100 c.c.* Na.	K.	Ca.	Mg.	Fe.	Cu.	P.	S.	Cl.	*Acid-base balance, c.c per 100 c.c.* N/10 Acid.	N/10 Alkali.
472	Mild ale, draught ..	0·5	Tr.	3·1	45	23·2	42	11·7	7·7	0·05	0·13	14·9	20·4	36·2		1
473	Mild ale, bottled ..	0·3	Tr.	3·7	49	19·4	54	12·7	10·0	0·08	0·07	18·1	25·2	36·1	1	
474	Pale ale, draught ..	0·3	Tr.	3·2	55	13·5	56	10·9	10·5	0·05	0·08	21·5	23·2	35·4	4	
475	Pale ale, bottled ..	0·2	Tr.	3·0	55	13·5	52	13·6	10·5	0·07	0·06	17·7	23·8	31·6	<1	
476	Strong ale	0·5	Tr.	4·9	76	19·3	89	16·9	14·4	0·10	0·11	28·5	34·1	54·4	3	
477	Stout	0·4	Tr.	4·1	50	20·9	68	10·3	11·6	0·14	0·12	23·3	23·2	35·7		2

Condiments—*continued*

No.	Food.	*g. per 100 g.* Protein (N× 6·25).	Fat.	Available carbohydrate (as monosaccharides).	Calories per 100 g.	*mg. per 100 g.* Na.	K.	Ca.	Mg.	Fe.	Cu.	P.	S.	Cl.	*Acid-base balance, c.c. per 100 g.* N/10 Acid.	N/10 Alkali.
478	Curry powder	9·5	10·8	26·1	237	450	1830	637	284	75·00	1·04	270	86	470		860
479	Ground ginger	7·4	3·3*	60·0	259	34	910	97	132	17·20	0·45	136	145	40		216
480	Mustard	28·9	28·7	20·7	463	5	943	333	256	10·90	0·20	177	1280	62	308	
481	Pepper	8·8	6·5†	68·0	309	7	42	127	45	10·20	1·13	130	99	60		289
482	Salt, block	0·0	0·0	0·0	0	38,700	Tr.	230	135	0·26	0·39	Tr.	401	59,600	107	
483	Table salt "A" ..	0·0	0·0	0·0	0	38,900	Tr.	149	500	0·54	0·55	74	35	60,000		422
484	Table salt "B" ..	0·0	0·0	0·0	0	39,300	Tr.	12	176	0·30	0·66	Tr.	23	60,300		139
485	Vinegar	0·4	0·0	0·6	4	20	89	15	22	0·47	0·04	32	19	47		12

* By Soxhlet extraction. The figure for fat obtained by von Lieberman's method is 0·4 per cent. and this has been used for calculating calories.

† By Soxhlet extraction. The figure for fat obtained by von Lieberman's method is 2·0 per cent. and this has been used for calculating calories.

Vegetable Fats

No.	Food.	Description and number of samples.	g. per 100 g.	
			Water.	Total nitrogen.
486	Margarine	4 samples from different shops	13·7	0·03
487	Olive oil	One sample only	Tr.	Tr.

Cakes and Pastries

No.	Food.	Description.	g. per 100 g.			
			Water.	Sugar (as invert sugar).	Starch and dextrins (as glucose).	Total nitrogen.
488	Buns (1943)	5 samples from different shops	27·2	9·5	47·5	1·55
489	Cherry cake	Recipe, p. 11	10·7	36·3	20·2	0·79
490	Chocolate cakes	Recipe, p. 11	12·9	31·4	24·5	1·08
491	Coconut cakes	Recipe, p. 11	12·7	16·7	38·0	1·19
492	Currant buns (1936)	20 samples from 4 different shops	28·6	14·0	40·5	1·30
493	Currant cake	Recipe, p. 11	12·7	31·1	29·8	1·01
494	Currant cake (1943)	4 samples from different shops	30·7	20·8	30·8	1·16
495	Doughnuts	16 samples from 4 different shops	26·4	15·0	33·8	1·05
496	Dundee cake	4 samples from different shops	15·2	42·0	20·3	0·65
497	Eccles cakes	Recipe, p. 12	14·5	16·0	35·6	0·82
498	Ginger biscuits	Recipe, p. 12	7·9	33·7	37·5	1·00
499	Gingerbread	Recipe, p. 12	19·0	32·7	30·7	0·94
500	Ginger cake (1943)	2 samples from different shops	30·7	12·4	42·0	1·18
501	Jam tarts, flaky pastry	Recipe, p. 12	25·5	37·2	19·3	0·46
502	Jam tarts, short pastry	Recipe, p. 12	23·0	37·3	23·9	0·56
503	Jam tarts, economical	M.O.F., recipe p. 12	10·0	24·2	40·2	1·03
504	Lemon curd tarts	Recipe, p. 12	22·4	17·6	33·0	0·95
505	Mince pies	Recipe, p. 12	34·9	9·4	33·2	0·75

Vegetable Fats—*continued*

No.	Food.	g. per 100 g. Protein (N × 6·25).	Fat.	Carbo-hydrate.	Calories per 100 g.	mg. per 100 g. Na.	K.	Ca.	Mg.	Fe.	Cu.	P.	S.	Cl.	Acid-base balance, c.c. per 100 g. N/10 Acid.	N/10 Alkali.
486	Margarine	0·2	85·3	0·0	794	(318)	5	4·1	0·9	0·30	0·04	12·0	12	(495)	13	
487	Olive oil	Tr.	99·9	0·0	929	0·1	Tr.	0·5	0·4	0·08	0·07	Tr.	Tr.	Tr.		<1

Cakes and Pastries—*continued*

No.	Food.	g. per 100 g. Protein	Fat.	Available carbohydrate (as monosaccharides).	Calories per 100 g.	mg. per 100 g. Na.	K.	Ca.	Mg.	Fe.	Cu.	P.	S.	Cl.	Acid-base balance, c.c. per 100 g. N/10 Acid.	N/10 Alkali.
488	Buns (1943)	8·9	6·1	57·0	307	(118)	198	(82)	46·0	2·71	0·32	170·0	—	(129)	—	—
489	Cherry cake	4·7	24·0	56·5	454	(137)	69	32·1	10·2	1·22	0·32	70·6	62·9	(127)	19	
490	Chocolate cakes	6·4	23·3	55·9	451	(217)	90	22·3	14·7	1·28	0·06	103·0	83·6	(179)	29	
491	Coconut cakes	7·0	23·4	54·7	450	(166)	174	35·0	22·8	1·09	0·10	101·5	82·7	(169)	11	
492	Currant buns (1936) ..	7·4	7·6	54·5	305	(101)	182	35·9	22·3	2·13	0·08	65·0	73·4	(195)	16	
493	Currant cake	5·9	18·4	60·9	422	(152)	208	34·4	17·6	1·15	0·14	85·0	76·8	(150)		6
494	Currant cake (1943) ..	6·6	10·8	51·6	321	(595)	210	(67)	34·1	2·44	0·27	(328)	—	(336)	—	—
495	Doughnuts	6·0	15·8	48·8	355	(60)	113	21·3	16·4	1·62	0·11	55·0	56·4	(89)	17	
496	Dundee cake	3·8	15·0	62·3	389	(141)	338	50·3	27·5	2·02	0·18	78·5	55·0	(180)		60
497	Eccles cakes	4·8	29·3	51·6	485	(167)	180	24·8	16·5	0·82	0·12	57·3	59·4	(275)	7	
498	Ginger biscuits	5·9	16·7	71·2	446	(331)	142	21·3	15·2	1·26	0·07	75·9	81·3	(141)		64
499	Gingerbread	5·5	13·0	63·4	381	(336)	160	35·5	15·4	1·26	0·07	81·0	78·1	(104)		87
500	Ginger cake (1943) ..	6·7	9·0	54·4	315	(970)	150	(69)	38·5	4·70	0·23	(469)	—	(327)	—	—
501	Jam tarts, flaky pastry ..	2·6	15·8	56·5	370	(103)	94	15·0	10·1	0·95	0·12	36·3	31·0	(158)	3	
502	Jam tarts, short pastry ..	3·2	13·3	61·0	365	(116)	102	15·9	11·4	0·99	0·12	41·9	36·9	(178)	6	
503	Jam tarts, economical ..	6·0	19·8	64·4	451	(165)	122	(128)	27·7	1·66	0·33	(236)	—	(159)	—	—
504	Lemon curd tarts ..	5·6	24·3	50·6	439	(175)	88	16·0	12·2	0·74	0·04	70·2	66·8	(275)	48	
505	Mince pies	4·4	19·7	42·6	361	(225)	267	27·8	17·9	1·22	0·05	50·2	57·8	(407)		12

Cakes and Pastries—*continued*

No.	Food.	Description.	g. per 100 g.			
			Water.	*Sugar (as invert sugar).*	*Starch and dextrins (as glucose).*	*Total nitrogen.*
506	Oatmeal biscuits	Recipe, p. 12	3·9	11·8	50·8	1·51
507	Oatmeal biscuits, economical	M.O.F. recipe, p. 12	2·0	8·0	65·6	1·68
508	Orange cake	Recipe, p. 13	13·7	28·0	26·0	1·01
509	Pastry, flaky, raw	Recipe, p. 13	32·0	Tr.	35·8	0·78
510	Pastry, flaky, baked	Recipe, p. 13	17·4	Tr.	43·5	0·95
511	Pastry, short, raw	Recipe, p. 13	27·2	Tr.	44·5	0·96
512	Pastry, short, baked	Recipe, p. 13	10·6	Tr.	54·8	1·17
513	Pastry, economical, raw	M.O.F. recipe, p. 13	19·1	Tr.	49·5	1·25
514	Pastry, economical, baked	M.O.F. recipe, p. 13	5·0	Tr.	59·9	1·51
515	Pastry, potato, raw	M.O.F. recipe, p. 13	31·8	0·1	48·6	1·20
516	Pastry, potato, baked	M.O.F. recipe, p. 13	10·7	0·2	63·5	1·57
517	Plain biscuits, economical	Recipe, p. 13	1·0	21·9	49·0	1·60
518	Plain cake, economical	M.O.F. recipe, p. 13	20·7	21·7	31·2	1·21
519	Queen cakes	Recipe, p. 13	11·3	32·0	27·1	1·02
520	Rock buns	Recipe, p. 13	11·3	27·4	37·6	0·96
521	Rock cakes	Recipe, p. 14	10·4	30·9	34·7	1·02
522	Rock cakes, economical	Recipe, p. 14	14·0	25·9	39·0	1·33
523	Scones (with egg)	Recipe, p. 14	20·4	9·4	50·6	1·47
524	Scones (without egg)	Recipe, p. 14	21·5	4·2	53·1	1·34
525	Shortbread	Recipe, p. 14	5·0	16·1	48·8	1·06
526	Sponge cake	Recipe, p. 14	30·0	31·4	23·7	1·52
527	Swiss roll (1943)	3 samples from different shops	34·0	34·7	22·4	0·95
528	Welsh cheese cakes	Recipe, p. 14	15·4	31·2	29·0	0·79

Cakes and Pastries—*continued*

No.	Food.	Protein (g. per 100 g.)	Fat. (g. per 100 g.)	Available carbohydrate (as monosaccharides). (g. per 100 g.)	Calories per 100 g.	Na. (mg. per 100 g.)	K.	Ca.	Mg.	Fe.	Cu.	P.	S.	Cl.	Acid-base balance, c.c. per 100 g. N/10 Acid.	N/10 Alkali.
506	Oatmeal biscuits ..	8·9	23·9	62·6	503	(277)	200	35·8	52·6	2·15	0·13	204·5	110·0	(136)	6	
507	Oatmeal biscuits, economical	9·6	18·6	73·6	488	(121)	245	(71)	72·1	2·89	0·27	251·0	—	(214)	—	—
508	Orange cake	5·9	25·5	54·0	463	(199)	91	20·6	11·6	0·98	0·05	87·5	78·4	(189)	29	
509	Pastry, flaky, raw ..	4·5	29·4	35·8	425	(178)	66	9·7	10·9	0·52	0·04	49·4	52·9	(287)	37	
510	Pastry, flaky, baked ..	5·4	35·8	43·5	518	(217)	80	11·7	13·3	0·63	0·05	60·0	64·1	(351)	46	
511	Pastry, short, raw ..	5·5	24·7	44·5	418	(202)	82	11·4	13·5	0·60	0·05	59·8	63·8	(325)	44	
512	Pastry, short, baked ..	6·7	30·4	54·8	515	(248)	100	14·0	16·5	0·74	0·06	73·5	78·5	(399)	54	
513	Pastry, economical, raw	7·2	24·3	49·5	441	(198)	106	(151)	31·9	1·59	0·24	(284)	—	(194)	—	—
514	Pastry, economical, baked	8·6	29·3	59·9	532	(238)	128	(183)	38·4	1·93	0·29	(343)	—	(235)	—	—
515	Pastry, potato, raw ..	7·0	14·6	48·7	348	(383)	182	(47)	33·0	1·53	0·22	105·0	—	(615)	—	—
516	Pastry, potato, baked ..	9·1	19·1	63·7	453	(498)	238	(62)	43·0	1·99	0·31	137·0	—	(804)	—	—
517	Plain biscuits, economical	9·4	21·1	70·9	500	(153)	131	(127)	33·2	2·04	0·25	(266)	—	(161)	—	—
518	Plain cake, economical ..	7·2	19·9	52·9	413	(154)	110	(121)	23·5	1·46	0·20	(235)	—	(162)	—	—
519	Queen cakes	6·0	22·4	59·1	454	(162)	173	32·4	15·4	1·06	0·09	94·1	79·4	(132)	4	
520	Rock buns	5·6	16·8	65·0	422	(155)	190	48·9	18·7	0·72	0·11	78·3	63·3	(144)		26
521	Rock cakes	6·0	16·0	65·6	418	(150)	240	42·3	20·1	1·09	0·15	83·6	74·0	(135)		27
522	Rock cakes, economical	7·8	12·8	64·9	394	(145)	278	(154)	34·2	1·88	0·28	(284)	—	(120)	—	—
523	Scones (with egg) ..	8·6	10·5	60·0	358	(169)	148	47·2	20·0	0·97	0·07	117·5	106·1	(127)	26	
524	Scones (without egg) ..	7·7	13·2	57·3	369	(165)	162	63·1	21·5	0·66	0·08	109·5	85·3	(125)		4
525	Shortbread	6·1	27·2	64·9	519	(86)	93	15·7	15·2	0·62	0·06	69·2	69·1	(141)	46	
526	Sponge cake	8·9	7·0	55·1	308	79	115	34·9	13·4	1·61	0·04	144·5	123·0	103	107	
527	Swiss roll (1943) ..	5·4	2·5	57·1	260	(652)	131	(72)	23·1	2·53	0·56	(353)	—	(244)	—	—
528	Welsh cheese cakes ..	4·7	18·9	60·2	421	(138)	100	17·5	12·4	0·99	0·10	61·5	56·8	(141)	10	

Puddings

No.	Food.	Description.	g. per 100 g.			
			Water.	*Sugar (as invert sugar).*	*Starch and dextrins (as glucose).*	*Total nitrogen.*
529	Apple Charlotte	Recipe, p. 14	51·0	20·9	7·7	0·22
530	Apple dumpling	Recipe, p. 15	58·1	11·6	16·9	0·39
531	Apple pudding	Recipe, p. 15	51·2	12·5	19·7	0·45
532	Apple tart	Recipe, p. 15	55·1	18·0	15·3	0·36
533	Banana custard	Recipe, p. 15	73·3	14·1	4·1	0·40
534	Blancmange	Recipe, p. 15	73·7	12·2	6·6	0·51
535	Bread pudding, economical	Recipe, p. 15	41·4	13·6	26·6	1·04
536	Bread and butter pudding	Recipe, p. 15	67·2	11·4	5·8	0·89
537	Cabinet pudding, steamed	Recipe, p. 15	67·9	14·2	6·4	0·74
538	Canary pudding, baked	Recipe, p. 16	13·3	26·1	29·4	1·08
539	Castle pudding, baked	Recipe, p. 16	16·2	25·1	28·8	1·03
540	Castle pudding, steamed	Recipe, p. 16	24·9	21·9	25·0	0·89
541	Chocolate mould	Recipe, p. 16	70·5	14·1	7·8	0·53
542	College pudding, baked	Recipe, p. 16	14·7	36·5	12·2	0·73
543	Custard, egg, baked	Recipe, p. 16	77·7	9·9	0·0	0·84
544	Custard, egg, boiled	Recipe, p. 16	75·9	13·4	0·0	0·75
545	Custard, powder, boiled	Recipe, p. 16	74·7	12·8	4·7	0·54
546	Custard tart	Recipe, p. 16	52·9	8·0	20·1	0·88
547	Dumpling	Recipe, p. 16	60·2	Tr.	24·0	0·53
548	Gooseberry tart	Recipe, p. 17	74·3	14·9	16·8	0·45
549	Gooseberry tart with potato pastry	Recipe, p. 17	63·6	2·0	21·8	0·64
550	Jam omelette	Recipe, p. 17	47·5	27·0	0·0	1·52
551	Jam roll, baked	Recipe, p. 17	20·4	21·0	34·4	0·77

Puddings—*continued*

No.	Food.	Protein (g. per 100 g.)	Fat. (g. per 100 g.)	Available carbohydrate (as monosaccharides) (g. per 100 g.)	Calories per 100 g.	Na. (mg. per 100 g.)	K.	Ca.	Mg.	Fe.	Cu.	P.	S.	Cl.	Acid-base balance, c.c per 100 g. $\frac{N}{10}$ Acid.	$\frac{N}{10}$ Alkali.
529	Apple Charlotte	1·3	16·0	28·6	262	(74)	99	7·2	5·4	0·43	0·10	22·4	12·6	(109)		13
530	Apple dumpling	2·2	9·3	28·5	202	(39)	109	6·6	6·9	0·41	0·09	32·8	25·8	(69)	3	
531	Apple pudding	2·6	12·7	32·2	250	(48)	76	6·3	6·9	0·36	0·06	30·8	30·2	20		5
532	Apple tart	2·1	8·7	33·3	214	(71)	92	5·9	6·3	0·36	0·06	29·2	23·7	(115)	3	
533	Banana custard ..	2·5	2·6	18·2	103	31	227	83·9	23·7	0·24	0·09	75·1	24·2	93		44
534	Blancmange	3·2	3·7	18·8	118	45	154	117·0	13·4	0·17	0·04	94·5	28·3	97		23
535	Bread pudding, economical	6·2	11·2	40·2	280	(211)	202	(60)	24·8	1·58	0·18	(133)	—	(233)	—	—
536	Bread and butter pudding	5·5	8·0	17·2	162	(113)	197	118·0	17·3	0·64	0·08	124·0	58·6	(190)		3
537	Cabinet pudding ..	4·5	4·5	20·6	138	(107)	196	86·9	16·1	0·64	0·05	98·1	34·8	(161)		23
538	Canary pudding	6·4	24·5	55·5	470	(172)	91	25·9	12·5	0·95	0·05	93·7	80·6	(142)	29	
539	Castle pudding, baked ..	6·1	23·7	53·9	457	(166)	84	22·1	11·7	0·91	0·04	87·9	78·0	(135)	29	
540	Castle pudding, steamed	5·2	20·6	46·9	388	(144)	73	19·1	10·2	0·79	0·04	76·5	67·8	(118)	26	
541	Chocolate mould ..	3·3	3·8	21·9	131	58	158	112·0	15·8	0·35	0·06	98·3	29·0	98		26
542	College pudding ..	4·3	24·0	48·7	423	(269)	232	33·1	15·3	1·19	0·13	74·7	58·0	(182)		70
543	Custard, egg, baked ..	5·2	5·9	9·9	113	65	175	127·0	15·2	0·51	0·05	130·0	58·3	123	5	
544	Custard, egg, boiled ..	4·7	5·3	13·4	119	58	156	113·0	13·7	0·46	0·04	116·0	52·0	110	5	
545	Custard, powder ..	3·4	3·9	17·5	116	46	160	122·0	13·9	0·15	0·04	98·0	29·6	100		24
546	Custard tart	5·4	14·4	28·1	262	(129)	133	72·7	14·7	0·56	0·04	96·9	60·1	(212)	21	
547	Dumpling	3·0	11·1	24·0	206	(488)	45	6·2	7·3	0·32	0·03	31·3	36·8	(626)		14
548	Gooseberry tart	2·6	9·4	31·7	217	(76)	136	18·6	8·7	0·39	0·08	39·5	32·0	(124)		4
549	Gooseberry tart, with potato pastry	3·8	6·6	23·8	166	(173)	202	(38)	17·0	0·87	0·18	66·4	—	(280)	—	—
550	Jam omelette	9·5	14·6	27·0	275	(121)	139	48·9	11·7	1·91	0·07	176·0	137·5	(145)	118	
551	Jam roll, baked	4·4	19·0	55·4	402	(151)	96	14·3	12·8	0·84	0·10	51·6	50·7	(137)		5

Puddings—*continued*

No.	Food.	Description.	*g. per 100 g.* Water.	Sugar (as invert sugar).	Starch and dextrins (as glucose).	Total nitrogen.
552	Jelly	Recipe, p. 17	78·6	19·1	0·0	0·34
553	Jelly, milk	Recipe, p. 17	72·7	20·9	0·0	0·59
554	Pancakes	Recipe, p. 17	43·4	20·5	16·9	0·82
555	Plum tart (weighed with stones)	Recipe, p. 17	72·5	16·0	16·8	0·40
556	Queen of puddings	Recipe, p. 17	59·1	17·3	6·4	0·87
557	Rhubarb tart	Recipe, p. 18	76·5	13·7	16·8	0·41
558	Rice pudding	Recipe, p. 18	64·5	11·5	9·9	0·72
559	Rice pudding, economical	Recipe, p. 18	73·2	8·8	10·2	0·78
560	Sago pudding	Recipe, p. 18	72·3	12·0	8·9	0·50
561	Semolina pudding	Recipe, p. 18	71·7	12·5	7·7	0·71
562	Suet pudding, plain	Recipe, p. 18	37·0	14·8	22·5	0·69
563	Suet pudding with raisins	Recipe, p. 18	34·5	22·1	19·4	0·61
564	Suet pudding with sultanas, economical	Recipe, p. 18	46·8	18·6	20·2	0·69
565	Syrup sponge pudding, economical	M.O.F. Recipe, p. 18	27·7	31·3	22·5	0·88
566	Tapioca pudding	Recipe, p. 19	71·7	12·2	9·2	0·51
567	Treacle tart	Recipe, p. 19	21·0	34·6	28·0	0·62
568	Trifle	Recipe, p. 19	63·8	21·5	6·6	0·61
569	Yorkshire pudding	Recipe, p. 19	56·4	3·5	23·5	1·15
570	Yorkshire pudding, economical	M.O.F. recipe, p. 19	52·6	Tr.	28·1	1·02

Puddings—*continued*

No.	Food.	g. per 100 g. Protein	Fat.	Available carbohydrate (as monosaccharides).	Calories per 100 g.	mg. per 100 g. Na.	K.	Ca.	Mg.	Fe.	Cu.	P.	S.	Cl.	Acid-base balance, c.c. per 100 g. $\frac{N}{10}$ Acid.	$\frac{N}{10}$ Alkali.
552	Jelly	*1·9	0	19·1	79	8	7	9·6	1·4	0·53	0·06	2·2	11·2	9		<1
553	Jelly, milk	*3·5	1·9	20·9	110	33	87	69·1	8·4	0·55	0·07	49·4	25·5	58		14
554	Pancakes	5·0	15·1	37·4	301	(88)	129	73·1	13·8	0·52	0·05	92·8	56·1	(151)	18	
555	Plum tart (weighed with stones)	2·3	9·4	32·8	219	(76)	119	10·6	8·7	0·36	0·06	29·0	26·1	(122)		7
556	Queen of puddings ..	5·1	9·8	23·7	200	(123)	145	86·8	14·4	0·85	0·06	112·0	59·8	(187)	16	
557	Rhubarb tart	2·3	9·4	30·5	210	(76)	244	55·9	12·0	0·43	0·08	32·8	28·0	(165)		48
558	Rice pudding	4·4	9·3	21·4	185	(62)	189	138·0	16·8	0·14	0·05	120·0	42·5	(133)		17
559	Rice pudding, economical	4·8	2·6	19·0	115	(80)	169	149·0	14·5	0·13	0·17	135·0	—	(149)	—	—
560	Sago pudding	3·1	3·7	20·9	125	48	152	119·0	13·5	0·18	0·04	91·2	27·6	94		28
561	Semolina pudding ..	4·3	3·9	20·2	130	50	174	120·0	17·0	0·19	0·05	104·6	37·9	103		17
562	Suet pudding, plain ..	3·9	18·1	37·3	324	(202)	95	44·6	12·3	0·41	0·04	59·7	40·0	(156)		38
563	Suet pudding with raisins	3·5	15·6	41·5	315	(181)	205	46·0	16·4	0·58	0·07	55·5	37·5	(134)		71
564	Suet pudding with sultanas, economical	4·1	9·0	38·8	246	(71)	185	(111)	19·8	0·93	0·17	(176)	—	41	—	—
565	Syrup sponge pudding, economical	5·2	14·3	53·8	356	(164)	126	(93)	18·7	1·33	0·14	(174)	—	(124)	—	—
566	Tapioca pudding ..	3·2	3·8	21·4	128	49	156	116·0	13·8	0·98	0·04	95·2	28·4	96		24
567	Treacle tart	3·5	13·5	62·6	374	(259)	160	19·4	11·7	1·03	0·07	46·3	62·9	(241)		36
568	Trifle	3·7	3·9	28·1	157	(50)	152	99·2	13·5	0·44	0·05	95·8	39·5	(91)		10
569	Yorkshire pudding ..	7·1	9·4	27·0	218	(412)	175	101·4	18·4	0·68	0·06	128·5	76·0	(662)	28	
570	Yorkshire pudding, economical	6·0	11·3	28·1	235	(554)	81	(154)	21·2	1·26	0·21	(296)	—	(705)	—	—

* *See* p. 6.

Meat and Fish Dishes

No.	Food.	Description.	g. per 100 g.		
			Water.	*Total nitrogen.*	*Purine nitrogen.*
571	Beef steak pudding	Recipe, p. 19	58·8	1·67	0·022
572	Beef stew	Recipe, p. 19	79·3	1·82	0·032
573	Curried meat	Recipe, p. 19	69·3	1·31	0·018
574	Fish cakes	Recipe, p. 20	71·2	2·03	0·036
575	Fish cakes, economical	M.O.F. recipe, p. 20	73·0	1·70	0·029
576	Fish pie	Recipe, p. 20	66·2	1·48	0·022
577	Hot pot	Recipe, p. 20	72·1	1·61	0·025
578	Irish stew	Recipe, p. 20	76·0	0·63	0·011
578*a*	Irish stew (weighed with bones)	Recipe, p. 20	70·0	0·58	0·010
579	Kedgeree	Recipe, p. 20	68·4	1·98	0·022
580	Sausage roll, flaky pastry	Recipe, p. 20	23·0	1·16	—
581	Sausage roll, short pastry	Recipe, p. 20	21·8	1·30	—
582	Sausage roll, short pastry, economical	Recipe, p. 20	16·2	1·71	—
583	Sausage roll, potato pastry	Recipe, p. 20	26·9	1·63	—
584	Shepherd's pie	Recipe, p. 21	75·7	1·17	0·015
585	Steak and kidney pie	Recipe, p. 21	48·8	2·52	0·049
586	Toad-in-the-hole	Recipe, p. 21	52·5	1·23	—

Meat and Fish Dishes—*continued*

No.	Food.	g. per 100 g.			Calories per 100 g.	mg. per 100 g.									Acid-base balance, c.c per 100 g.	
		Protein	Fat.	Available carbohydrate (as glucose).		Na.	K.	Ca.	Mg.	Fe.	Cu.	P.	S.	Cl.	$\frac{N}{10}$ Acid.	$\frac{N}{10}$ Alkali.
571	Beef steak pudding ..	10·2	13·1	21·6	245	(787)	166	7·4	15·6	1·87	—	132	107	(1120)	67	
572	Beef stew	11·1	5·8	2·5	108	(718)	233	13·5	16·4	2·49	—	160	119	(1070)	88	
573	Curried meat	7·9	11·1	8·7	168	(294)	252	32·7	20·4	4·70	—	101	98	(436)	24	
574	Fish cakes	12·1	13·9	9·8	216	(419)	298	19·6	18·4	0·78	0·14	170	145	(649)	92	
575	Fish cakes, economical ..	10·6	1·7	14·1	112	(352)	343	26·2	22·0	0·93	0·13	154	—	(541)	—	—
576	Fish pie	9·0	15·2	6·6	204	(513)	249	51·3	16·3	0·56	0·08	143	107	(793)	57	
577	Hot pot	9·7	4·6	11·3	125	(577)	464	21·9	25·2	2·33	—	149	117	(892)	19	
578	Irish stew	3·8	11·0	7·8	146	(356)	221	10·3	11·9	0·90	—	57	50	(559)		1
578*a*	Irish stew (weighed with bones)	3·5	10·2	7·3	136	(329)	205	9·4	11·0	0·83	—	53	46	(517)		1
579	Kedgeree	12·1	7·0	9·9	152	(1090)	161	21·0	23·8	1·03	—	169	158	(1610)	115	
580	Sausage roll, flaky pastry	7·3	36·0	35·5	497	(406)	111	13·4	13·5	1·30	0·07	80	71	(610)	46	
581	Sausage roll, short pastry	8·1	31·2	40·2	474	(450)	125	15·2	15·4	1·44	0·07	90	80	(667)	47	
582	Sausage roll, short pastry, economical	10·3	25·8	46·8	458	(442)	190	(146)	43·8	2·27	0·31	(307)	—	(540)	—	—
583	Sausage roll, potato pastry	9·8	18·1	45·7	380	(585)	246	(62)	43·9	2·16	0·30	159	—	(870)	—	—
584	Shepherd's pie	7·1	5·4	12·2	125	(370)	292	15·0	16·4	2·31	—	88	80	(583)	14	
585	Steak and kidney pie ..	15·4	18·9	16·7	302	(794)	243	10·1	20·9	5·57	—	213	157	(1192)	140	
586	Toad-in-the-hole ..	7·7	20·3	18·6	295	(699)	163	66·9	16·0	1·38	0·07	125	80	(1050)	33	

Egg and Cheese Dishes

No.	Food.	Description.	g. per 100 g.			
			Water.	*Sugar (as mono-saccharides).*	*Starch and dextrins (as glucose).*	*Total nitrogen.*
587	Buck rarebit	Recipe, p. 21	36·7	0·3	15·9	2·32
588	Cheese omelette	Recipe, p. 21	48·4	0·0	0·0	2·84
589	Cheese pudding, economical	M.O.F. recipe, p. 21	71·8	2·8	7·3	1·44
590	Cheese straws	Recipe, p. 21	11·2	Tr.	25·9	2·58
591	Macaroni cheese	Recipe, p. 21	63·9	2·6	12·6	1·22
592	Macaroni cheese, economical	M.O.F. recipe, p. 22	74·7	2·3	10·4	0·94
593	Omelette	Recipe, p. 22	60·3	0·0	0·0	1·20
594	Scotch egg	Recipe, p. 22	53·1	Tr.	10·3	1·78
595	Scrambled eggs	Recipe, p. 22	62·2	0·6	0·0	1·62
596	Scrambled eggs with dried eggs	M.O.F. recipe, p. 22	59·4	0·0	0·0	2·07
597	Welsh rarebit	Recipe, p. 22	26·9	0·4	20·3	2·43

Egg and Cheese Dishes—*continued*

No.	Food.	*g. per 100 g.* Protein	Fat.	Available carbohydrate (as monosaccharides).	Calories per 100 g.	*mg. per 100 g.* Na.	K.	Ca.	Mg.	Fe.	Cu.	P.	S.	Cl.	*Acid-base balance, c.c. per 100 g.* $\frac{N}{10}$ Acid.	$\frac{N}{10}$ Alkali.
587	Buck rarebit	14·5	30·5	16·2	404	(431)	123	333·0	28·4	1·09	0·05	284	144	(688)	57	
588	Cheese omelette	17·8	30·9	Tr.	361	(1420)	149	316·0	25·8	2·20	0·06	356	214	(2180)	140	
589	Cheese pudding, economical	8·9	7·4	10·1	143	(491)	139	195·0	21·3	0·87	0·13	194	—	(766)	—	—
590	Cheese straws	16·4	47·5	25·7	606	(824)	113	408·0	31·2	0·93	0·06	328	158	(1320)	70	
591	Macaroni cheese	7·6	12·8	15·2	207	(670)	137	199·0	25·5	0·35	0·04	162	70	(1060)		1
592	Macaroni cheese, economical	5·7	5·9	12·7	126	(260)	79	147·0	16·4	0·31	0·11	125	—	(444)	—	—
593	Omelette	7·6	30·3	0·0	314	(1010)	90	39·0	8·4	1·63	0·04	143	111	(1520)	102	
594	Scotch egg	11·1	19·3	10·3	263	(540)	165	35·6	13·9	2·72	0·09	166	126	(741)	89	
595	Scrambled eggs	10·1	25·2	0·6	279	(1260)	132	61·6	12·0	2·08	0·05	191	144	(1910)	125	
596	Scrambled eggs with dried eggs	12·9	25·9	0·0	294	(1510)	145	57·2	12·6	2·35	0·06	242	189	(2400)	215	
597	Welsh rarebit	15·2	35·5	20·7	470	(513)	118	409·0	32·6	0·69	0·06	302	135	(832)	28	

Sauces and Soups

No.	Food.	Description.	g. per 100 g.			
			Water.	*Sugar (as mono-saccharides).*	*Starch and dextrins (as glucose).*	*Total nitrogen.*
598	Bread sauce	Recipe, p. 22	76·0	4·0	8·9	0·65
599	Bone and vegetable broth* ..	Mean of 6 samples, analysed as served in hospital.	90·3	1·0	0·1	0·59
600	Bone and vegetable broth (Bickiepegs)*	Mean of 2 samples, analysed as purchased	—	0·3	Tr.	0·71
601	Cheese sauce	Recipe, p. 22	70·3	4·0	5·0	1·05
602	Egg sauce	Recipe, p. 23	75·4	3·8	4·8	0·79
603	Onion sauce	Recipe, p. 23	84·4	3·9	3·2	0·39
604	Potato soup	Recipe, p. 23	81·4	2·5	8·6	0·34
605	Soup	Mean of 7 samples, analysed as served in hospital.	89·9	1·5	2·8	0·32
606	White sauce, savoury	Recipe, p. 23	75·7	4·4	5·6	0·61
607	White sauce, sweet	Recipe, p. 23	69·3	13·1	5·1	0·56

* See McCance, Sheldon and Widdowson (1934).

Vegetable Dishes

No.	Food.	Description.	g. per 100 g.			
			Water.	*Sugar (as mono-saccharides).*	*Starch and dextrins (as glucose).*	*Total nitrogen.*
608	Potato cakes	M.O.F. recipe, p. 23	61·7	0·4	34·8	0·61
609	Vegetable pie with potato pastry ..	Recipe, p. 23	70·4	1·9	19·7	0·44

No.	Food.	g. per 100 g. Protein	Fat.	Available carbohydrate (as monosaccharides).	Calories per 100 g.	mg. per 100 g. Na.	K.	Ca.	Mg.	Fe.	Cu.	P.	S.	Cl.	Acid-base balance, c.c. per 100 g. $\frac{N}{10}$ Acid.	$\frac{N}{10}$ Alkali.
598	Bread sauce	4·0	5·1	12·9	113	(325)	153	104·0	15·5	0·22	0·04	92·0	33·9	(515)		20
599	Bone and vegetable broth	3·7	4·6	1·1	62	(74)	64	16·9	3·2	0·28	0·04	9·9	—	(75)	—	—
600	Bone and vegetable broth (Bickiepegs)	4·4	—	0·3	—	49	42	10·2	3·9	0·28	0·03	7·0	—	57	—	—
601	Cheese sauce	6·6	13·0	9·0	182	(546)	160	203·0	19·2	0·21	0·04	150·0	60·5	(873)	5	15
602	Egg sauce	4·9	10·1	8·6	146	(467)	158	105·0	14·5	0·49	0·04	113·0	54·9	(732)		
603	Onion sauce	2·4	5·6	7·1	88	(307)	128	76·4	10·8	0·20	0·06	63·1	27·7	(482)		20
604	Potato soup	2·1	4·4	11·1	91	(328)	95	46·0	15·8	0·39	0·08	52·0	29·4	(542)	1	
605	Soup, mixed	2·0	1·3	4·3	36	(218)	134	33·8	7·2	1·39	0·01	40·0	—	(390)	—	—
606	White sauce, savoury ..	3·7	9·7	10·0	143	(523)	161	113·0	14·8	0·15	0·04	96·2	35·6	(828)		20
607	White sauce, sweet ..	3·4	8·9	18·2	165	65	148	104·0	13·6	0·14	0·04	88·2	32·7	120		18

Vegetable Dishes—*continued*

No.	Food.	g. per 100 g. Protein	Fat.	Available carbohydrate (as monosaccharides).	Calories per 100 g.	mg. per 100 g. Na.	K.	Ca.	Mg.	Fe.	Cu.	P.	S.	Cl.	Acid-base balance, c.c. per 100 g. $\frac{N}{10}$ Acid.	$\frac{N}{10}$ Alkali.
608	Potato cakes	3·6	0·4	35·2	151	(621)	367	24·3	27·1	0·97	0·18	63·0	—	(996)	—	—
609	Vegetable pie with potato pastry	2·8	3·5	21·6	125	(425)	350	34·4	22·0	0·82	0·14	50·0	—	(674)	—	—

COMPOSITION OF FOODS PER OUNCE

Cereals and Cereal Foods

No.	Food.	g. per oz. Protein (N × 5·7).	Fat.	Available carbohydrate (as monosaccharides).	Calories per oz.	mg. per oz. Na.	K.	Ca.	Mg.	Fe.	Cu.	P.	S.	Cl.	Acid-base balance, c.c. per oz. $\frac{N}{10}$ Acid.	$\frac{N}{10}$ Alkali.
1	All-Bran, Kellogg's ..	3·6	1·3	16·5	88	(345)	271	23·4	119·3	3·06	0·13	231·5	51·6	(574)	12	
2	Arrowroot	0·1	Tr.	26·7	101	1·4	5	2·0	2·2	0·55	0·06	7·8	0·5	2·0	1	
3	Barley, pearl, raw ..	2·2	0·5	23·7	102	0·7	35	2·8	5·7	0·19	0·03	58·3	30·5	29·7	50	
4	Barley, pearl, boiled ..	0·7	0·2	7·8	34	0·2	11	1·0	1·9	0·06	0·01	19·9	10·4	10·1	17	
5	Biscuits, cream crackers	2·4	9·4	16·3	158	(124)	36	5·1	5·4	0·27	0·04	23·2	22·1	(200)	15	
6	Biscuits, digestive (1935)	2·7	5·8	18·7	137	(124)	44	12·4	9·1	0·45	0·07	38·0	20·5	(123)		7
7	Biscuits, digestive (1944)	2·1	6·4	18·9	139	(123)	51	10·1	11·4	0·57	0·09	42·0	—	(107)	—	—
8	Biscuits, plain mixed (1936)	2·1	3·8	21·4	123	(69)	48	12·9	4·1	0·35	0·02	11·6	23·7	(74)		9
9	Biscuits, plain mixed (1944)	2·0	4·4	21·2	128	(126)	53	15·2	11·7	0·51	0·08	52·0	—	(95)	—	—
10	Biscuits, rusks	1·7	2·4	23·2	116	(59)	40	24·6	7·7	0·76	0·06	22·8	30·5	(49)		7
11	Biscuits, sweet, mixed ..	1·6	8·7	18·9	158	(61)	39	7·7	4·0	0·24	0·03	18·8	9·1	(105)	4	
12	Biscuits, water	3·0	3·5	20·7	126	(134)	40	6·3	5·4	0·27	0·04	24·6	28·4	(192)	11	
13	Bread, currant (1936) ..	1·8	1·0	14·7	71	(47)	71	10·7	7·0	0·67	0·03	34·4	16·9	(81)	6	
14	Bread, Hovis (1936) ..	3·0	1·1	13·3	71	(129)	69	7·8	22·4	0·84	0·03	73·0	22·0	(182)	16	
15	Bread, malt (1936) ..	2·4	0·9	14·0	71	(78)	108	15·0	22·0	0·91	0·02	71·9	32·6	(149)	21	
16	Bread, brown (90%) ..	2·4	0·4	15·2	70	(112)	42	4·9	14·9	0·57	0·09	45·5	—	(172)	—	—
17	Bread, National wheatmeal (85%)	2·4	0·3	15·8	72	(112)	33	4·3	10·6	0·52	0·07	36·1	—	(172)	—	—
18	Bread (80%)	2·4	0·3	16·3	74	(112)	27	3·8	7·6	0·45	0·06	27·8	—	(172)	—	—
19	Bread, white (70%) ..	2·3	0·2	16·9	75	(112)	20	3·2	4·7	0·41	0·04	19·6	—	(172)	—	—
20	Bread, white, toasted ..	2·7	0·3	20·0	89	(133)	24	3·8	5·5	0·48	0·05	23·3	—	(204)	—	—
21	Bread, white, fried ..	2·0	10·6	14·9	163	(99)	18	2·9	4·1	0·36	0·04	17·3	—	(152)	—	—
22	Cornflakes, Kellogg's ..	1·9	0·2	25·2	104	(298)	32	2·1	4·7	0·80	0·03	16·5	26·2	(432)	6	
23	Cornflour	0·1	0·2	26·2	100	14·7	17	4·4	2·0	0·41	0·04	11·1	0·3	20·2		2
24	Custard powder ..			Take as	Cornfl	our.										
25	Flour, English (100%) ..	2·5	0·6	20·8	95	1·0	103	10·1	30·1	0·87	0·18	96·6	—	10·1	—	—
26	Flour, English (85%) ..	2·4	0·4	22·5	98	0·8	51	7·0	10·0	0·63	0·10	43·5	—	12·0	—	—
27	Flour, English (80%) ..	2·3	0·4	22·9	99	0·6	43	6·1	6·8	0·47	0·08	33·5	—	12·6	—	—
28	Flour, English (75%) ..	2·3	0·3	23·2	99	0·6	34	5·5	4·8	0·38	0·06	26·4	—	12·7	—	—

29	Flour, English (70%) ..	2·2	0·3	23·3	99	0·6	32	5·4	3·9	0·40	0·06	23·8	—	12·8	—	—
30	Flour, English (patent) ..	2·2	0·2	23·7	100	—	28	4·3	2·5	0·27	0·06	19·3	—	11·8	—	—
31	Flour, Manitoba (100%)	3·9	0·7	19·7	96	0·9	89	7·8	40·0	1·08	0·17	99·5	—	10·9	—	—
32	Flour, Manitoba (85%) ..	3·9	0·5	21·0	99	1·2	41	5·3	17·5	0·77	0·10	53·5	—	12·6	—	—
33	Flour, Manitoba (80%) ..	3·8	0·4	21·5	99	0·8	32	4·4	12·7	0·70	0·08	39·5	—	13·8	—	—
34	Flour, Manitoba (75%) ..	3·7	0·4	21·7	100	—	25	3·7	8·6	0·65	0·06	31·0	—	13·6	—	—
35	Flour, Manitoba (70%) ..	3·6	0·3	21·8	100	0·6	23	3·6	7·6	0·63	0·05	27·6	—	13·6	—	—
36	Flour, Manitoba (patent)	3·4	0·3	22·2	100	0·5	20	3·2	6·1	0·59	0·04	23·3	—	12·8	—	—
37	Flour, mixed grist, brown (90%)	3·3	0·5	21·1	98	1·0	58	6·8	20·7	0·80	0·13	63·5	—	11·6	—	—
38	Flour, mixed grist, National Wheatmeal (85%)	3·3	0·5	21·6	99	1·0	45	5·9	14·5	0·71	0·10	49·5	—	12·4	—	—
39	Flour, mixed grist (80%)	3·2	0·4	22·1	100	0·7	36	5·1	10·3	0·61	0·08	37·5	—	13·3	—	—
40	Flour, mixed grist, white (70%)	3·1	0·3	22·4	100	0·6	26	4·3	6·2	0·54	0·06	26·1	—	13·3	—	—
41	Force	2·6	0·5	23·8	105	(197)	115	18·8	42·1	1·13	0·10	96·3	29·6	(318)	11	
42	Grapenuts	3·3	0·9	21·4	102	(187)	121	13·6	43·4	1·60	0·05	94·6	41·1	(257)	4	
43	Macaroni (1936), raw ..	3·0	0·6	22·6	102	7·3	62	7·5	16·2	0·41	0·02	43·1	27·0	8·9	11	
44	Macaroni (1936), boiled ..	1·0	0·2	7·2	32	2·2	19	2·3	5·0	0·13	0·01	13·2	8·3	2·7	3	
45	Macaroni (1943), raw ..	3·3	0·4	22·1	100	(45)	40	5·8	11·9	0·37	0·09	40·1	—	43·5	—	—
46	Oatmeal, raw	3·4	2·5	20·6	115	9·5	104	15·8	32·0	1·17	0·07	108·0	44·0	20·8	38	
47	Oatmeal porridge ..	0·4	0·3	2·3	13	(164)	12	1·8	3·7	0·14	0·01	12·2	5·1	(253)	4	
48	Post Toasties	1·9	0·2	25·2	104	(230)	34	1·3	4·7	0·47	0·04	15·2	23·6	(344)	8	
49	Rice, polished, raw ..	1·8	0·3	24·6	102	1·8	32	1·1	3·7	0·13	0·02	28·0	22·4	7·7	22	
50	Rice, polished, boiled ..	0·6	0·1	8·4	35	0·6	11	0·4	1·3	0·04	0·01	9·5	7·6	2·6	7	
51	Rye (100%)	2·3	0·6	21·5	95	—	117	8·9	26·1	0·77	—	102·0	—	—	—	—
52	Rye (85%)	2·1	0·5	22·8	99	—	58	7·4	12·8	0·56	—	54·8	—	—	—	—
53	Rye (75%)	1·9	0·4	23·4	100	—	49	5·5	7·4	0·49	—	36·7	—	—	—	—
54	Rye (60%)	1·6	0·3	24·4	101	—	40	4·4	4·6	0·38	—	22·2	—	—	—	—
55	Ryvita	1·9	0·6	24·7	106	(175)	133	11·5	25·7	1·06	0·04	83·9	24·7	(266)	7	
56	Sago	0·1	0·1	26·7	101	1·0	1	2·8	0·7	0·34	0·01	8·1	0·1	3·6	4	
57	Semolina	3·0	0·5	22·0	100	3·4	47	5·2	9·1	0·30	0·04	32·4	26·0	20·2	19	
58	Shredded wheat	2·8	0·8	22·4	103	4·7	86	9·9	34·1	1·27	0·13	81·5	24·6	20·2	16	
59	Soya, full fat flour ..	11·5*	6·7	3·8†	123	—	472	59·3	66·8	1·97	—	169·5	—	—	—	—
60	Soya, low flat flour or grits.	14·1*	2·0	4·9†	95	—	575	68·5	81·2	2·60	—	183·0	—	—	—	—
61	Tapioca	0·1	Tr.	27·0	102	1·2	6	2·3	0·6	0·09	0·02	11·1	1·0	3·7	3	
62	Vita-Weat	2·4	2·9	22·1	120	(172)	122	12·5	33·4	0·97	0·05	105·8	26·5	(240)	12	

Note.—If flour is fortified with $CaCO_3$, add 18 mg. Ca per oz. flour.
*Total N × 6·25. † 75 per cent. total carbohydrate taken to be available.

Dairy Products

No	Food.	g. per oz.			Calories per oz.	mg. per oz.									Acid-base balance, c.c. per oz.	
		Protein (N × 6·25).	Fat.	Available carbohydrate (as monosaccharides).		Na.	K.	Ca.	Mg.	Fe.	Cu.	P.	S.	Cl.	$\frac{N}{10}$ Acid.	$\frac{N}{10}$ Alkali.
63	Butter, fresh	0·1	24·2	Tr.	226	(63)	4	4·2	0·7	0·05	0·01	6·8	2·6	(94)	1	
64	Cheese, Cheddar	7·1	9·8	Tr.	120	(174)	33	230·0	13·3	0·16	0·01	155·0	65·2	(300)	15	
65	Cheese, cream	0·9	24·5	Tr.	232	(31)	13	8·4	1·5	0·04	0·01	12·5	18·2	(43)	10	
66	Cheese, Dutch	8·0	4·8	Tr.	77	(355)	27	256·0	14·9	0·22	0·01	136·0	53·1	(582)		17
67	Cheese, Gorgonzola	7·1	8·8	Tr.	112	(347)	49	153·0	10·7	0·14	0·04	106·0	50·2	(511)	1	
68	Cheese, Gruyère	10·4	9·5	Tr.	131	(154)	36	306·0	12·8	0·07	0·08	198·0	58·5	(235)		10
69	Cheese, packet	6·4	8·5	Tr.	106	(260)	24	205·0	13·5	0·16	0·01	136·0	91·0	(308)		1
70	Cheese, Parmesan	9·8	8·4	Tr.	118	(215)	44	346·0	14·1	0·11	0·10	220·0	71·0	(315)		14
71	Cheese, St. Ivel	6·6	8·7	Tr.	108	(161)	19	137·0	6·6	0·20	0·01	106·0	52·9	(258)	25	
72	Cheese, Stilton	7·1	11·4	Tr.	135	(326)	46	102·0	7·7	0·13	0·01	86·2	64·5	(488)	22	
73	Cream	0·5	11·9	0·7	115	9·0	26	16·8	1·3	0·07	0·04	7·1	9·4	15·3		5
74	Egg white	2·6	Tr.	0·0	11	54·7	42	1·5	3·0	0·03	0·01	9·2	51·9	48·4	14	
75	Egg yolk	4·6	8·7	0·0	99	14·2	35	37·4	4·2	1·74	0·01	141·0	46·7	40·4	94	
76	Eggs, raw or boiled	3·4	3·5	0·0	46	38·4	39	15·9	3·5	0·72	0·01	62·0	49·1	45·2	46	
77	Eggs, dried	12·3	12·3	0·0	165	147·0	137	54·0	11·7	2·23	0·05	227·0	179·0	168·5	170	
78	Eggs, fried	4·0	5·5	0·0	68	62·4	50	18·2	3·9	0·72	0·01	72·7	58·4	56·5	47	
79	Eggs, poached	3·5	3·3	0·0	45	31·5	34	14·7	3·2	0·65	0·01	67·8	51·3	44·0	56	
80	Milk, fresh, whole	0·9	1·1	*1·4	19	14·2	46	34·1	4·0	0·02	0·01	27·0	8·3	27·8		8
81	Milk, fresh, skimmed	1·0	0·1	*1·4	10	14·8	47	35·2	4·1	0·02	0·01	27·8	8·5	28·9		8
82	Milk, condensed, whole, sweetened	2·3	3·4	15·9	100	40·7	116	97·5	10·2	0·05	0·02	68·0	23·5	81·0		24
83	Milk, condensed, whole, unsweetened	2·2	2·4	*3·5	44	45·8	143	82·5	9·9	0·05	0·03	72·0	21·3	79·0		24
84	Milk, condensed, skimmed, sweetened	2·8	0·1	17·0	76	51·0	142	109·0	10·7	0·08	0·01	76·8	26·8	88·0		31
85	Milk, dried, skimmed ("Household")	9·7	0·1	*14·0	93	170·0	378	359·0	31·5	0·15	0·40†	298·0	85·0	321·0		41
86	Milk, dried, whole	7·5	8·4	*11·0	150	113·0	363	272·0	31·8	0·18	0·05	215·0	66·1	222·0		61

* See p. 6. † Most of this copper was probably derived from the manufacturing machinery. See p. 9.

No.	Food.	g. per oz. Protein	Fat.	Carbohydrate (as glucose).	Calories per oz.	mg. per oz. Na.	K.	Ca.	Mg.	Fe.	Cu.	P.	S.	Cl.	Acid-base balance, c.c. per oz. $\frac{N}{10}$ Acid.	$\frac{N}{10}$ Alkali.
	Bacon, Raw—															
87	Danish Wilts., average	4·0	10·6	0·0	115	(348)	71	3·8	4·1	0·37	0·05	35	46	(530)	21	
88	Danish Wilts., fore end	4·2	9·0	0·0	101	(385)	75	4·1	4·4	0·30	0·06	39	48	(588)	30	
89	Danish Wilts., middle ..	3·7	12·7	0·0	133	(329)	64	3·8	3·9	0·37	0·05	34	43	(501)	14	
90	Danish Wilts., gammon	4·3	8·0	0·0	92	(342)	81	3·6	4·2	0·48	0·05	32	51	(533)	28	
91	English Wilts.	3·6	14·0	0·0	144	(277)	76	3·8	3·5	0·25	0·08	27	41	(428)	19	
92	English Midland ..	3·0	17·4	0·0	174	(236)	80	2·0	3·0	0·28	0·16	26	34	(370)	16	
93	Bacon, back, fried ..	7·0	15·2	0·0	169	(793)	147	3·3	7·3	0·80	—	65	85	(1180)	37	
94	Bacon, collar, fried ..	7·8	9·9	0·0	124	(866)	140	6·6	7·3	1·11	—	67	94	(1360)	64	
95	Bacon, gammon, fried ..	8·9	9·6	0·0	126	(662)	181	7·1	9·3	0·80	—	86	109	(1200)	116	
96	Bacon, streaky, fried ..	6·8	13·1	0·0	149	(880)	131	14·9	7·1	0·91	—	68	85	(1350)	48	
97	Beef, corned	6·3	4·3	0·0	66	(392)	33	3·6	8·2	2·78	—	34	60	(590)	39	
98	Beef, frozen, raw ..	5·8	2·1	0·0	43	21·0	100	2·3	7·1	1·05	0·05	57	61	21·0	39	
99	Beef, silverside, boiled ..	7·9	5·7	0·0	86	(417)	82	6·6	5·7	1·05	0·05	69	83	(660)	71	
100	Beef, sirloin, roast, lean only	7·6	3·5	0·0	64	19·9	101	1·8	7·1	1·50	0·05	81	80	21·0	66	
101	Beef, sirloin, roast, lean and fat	6·0	9·1	0·0	109	17·6	82	1·6	5·7	1·31	0·05	67	64	18·2	54	
102	Beef steak, raw	5·5	3·0	0·0	50	19·6	95	1·5	6·9	1·22	—	78	57	19·9	52	
103	Beef steak, fried ..	5·8	5·8	0·0	78	22·7	106	1·5	7·1	1·70	—	73	62	25·6	49	
104	Beef steak, grilled ..	7·2	6·1	0·0	86	19·0	105	2·6	7·2	1·48	—	86	76	18·2	66	
105	Beef steak, stewed ..	8·7	2·4	0·0	58	10·8	43	0·9	6·0	1·45	—	65	93	11·0	82	
106	Beef, topside, boiled ..	9·5	2·3	0·0	61	13·1	63	1·0	7·4	2·36	—	70	98	13·9	82	
107	Beef, topside, roast, lean only	7·6	4·3	0·0	71	21·6	105	1·8	8·0	1·34	0·07	81	79	17·6	63	
108	Beef, topside, roast, lean and fat	6·9	6·8	0·0	91	20·4	96	1·7	7·2	1·25	0·07	75	72	16·8	58	
109	Brain, calf, boiled ..	3·4	1·6	0·0	29	41·8	77	4·6	3·8	0·57	—	101	38	47·4	58	
110	Brain, sheep, boiled ..	3·3	1·9	0·0	31	48·3	76	3·1	5·1	0·63	—	96	37	40·9	58	
111	Chicken, boiled	7·4	2·9	0·0	58	27·8	108	3·0	7·5	0·60	—	77	83	17·6	59	
111*a*	Chicken, boiled (weighed with bone)	4·8	1·9	0·0	38	18·1	70	2·0	4·9	0·39	—	50	54	11·4	38	
112	Chicken, roast	8·4	2·1	0·0	54	22·7	101	4·1	6·5	0·74	—	77	92	28·4	72	
112*a*	Chicken, roast (weighed with bone)	4·5	1·1	0·0	29	12·2	55	2·2	3·5	0·40	—	42	50	15·4	39	
113	Dripping, beef	Tr.	28·1	0·0	262	1·4	1	0·2	Tr.	0·06	—	4	3	0·6	3	

Meat, Poultry and Game—*continued*

No.	Food.	Protein (g. per oz.)	Fat. (g. per oz.)	Carbohydrate (as glucose). (g. per oz.)	Calories per oz.	Na. (mg. per oz.)	K. (mg. per oz.)	Ca. (mg. per oz.)	Mg. (mg. per oz.)	Fe. (mg. per oz.)	Cu. (mg. per oz.)	P. (mg. per oz.)	S. (mg. per oz.)	Cl. (mg. per oz.)	$\frac{N}{10}$ Acid. (Acid-base balance, c.c. per oz.)	$\frac{N}{10}$ Alkali. (Acid-base balance, c.c. per oz.)
114	Duck, roast	6·5	6·7	0·0	89	55·3	90	5·4	6·8	1·64	—	66	112	44·9	69	
114*a*	Duck, roast (weighed with bone)	3·5	3·6	0·0	48	29·8	49	2·9	3·7	0·88	—	36	61	24·2	37	
115	Goose, roast	8·0	6·4	0·0	92	41·2	115	3·0	8·8	1·32	—	76	91	45·1	62	
115*a*	Goose, roast (weighed with bone)	4·6	3·7	0·0	53	23·8	67	1·7	5·1	0·77	—	44	53	26·1	36	
116	Grouse, roast	8·6	1·5	0·0	49	27·3	132	8·5	11·6	2·16	—	96	97	38·0	73	
116*a*	Grouse, roast (weighed with bone)	5·7	1·0	0·0	32	18·0	87	5·6	7·6	1·42	—	63	64	25·0	48	
117	Guinea fowl, roast ..	9·2	2·3	0·0	60	38·6	122	5·5	8·2	2·64	—	83	103	50·9	75	
117*a*	Guineafowl,roast(weighed with bone)	4·9	1·2	0·0	32	20·4	65	2·9	4·3	1·40	—	44	55	27·0	40	
118	Ham, York, raw ..	4·3	13·9	0·0	146	(320)	98	4·0	4·4	0·34	—	30	50	(503)	22	
119	Ham, boiled, lean only ..	6·6	3·8	0·0	62	(595)	129	4·8	6·7	0·74	—	69	80	(950)	63	
120	Ham, boiled, lean and fat	4·6	11·2	0·0	123	(422)	91	3·6	4·9	0·71	—	54	56	(665)	46	
121	Ham or Pork, chopped ..	4·3	8·5	Tr.	97	(438)	63	3·4	4·7	0·44	0·03	39	—	(602)	—	—
122	Hare, roast	8·9	2·0	0·0	55	15·0	115	8·0	8·5	2·78	0·07	96	99	30·6	85	
122*a*	Hare, roast (weighed with bone)	6·1	1·4	0·0	37	10·2	78	5·4	5·8	1·89	0·05	65	67	20·8	58	
123	Hare, stewed	8·3	2·3	0·0	55	11·4	60	5·9	6·3	3·07	—	71	91	21·0	80	
123*a*	Hare, stewed (weighed with bone)	6·1	1·7	0·0	40	8·3	44	4·3	4·6	2·24	—	51	66	15·3	58	
124	Heart, sheep, roast ..	7·1	4·2	0·0	68	43·5	105	2·7	9·9	2·30	—	111	84	35·5	78	
125	Kidney, ox, raw ..	4·8	1·5	0·0	34	69·5	66	4·0	5·2	4·25	—	74	46	72·7	43	
126	Kidney, ox, stewed ..	7·3	1·6	0·0	45	46·5	47	5·9	6·3	2·02	—	111	69	40·9	86	
127	Kidney, sheep, raw ..	4·8	0·9	0·0	34	71·0	72	3·8	4·5	3·32	—	72	47	83·8	45	
128	Kidney, sheep, fried ..	7·9	2·6	0·0	57	74·0	86	4·7	7·6	4·12	—	123	78	82·0	88	
129	Lard	Tr.	28·1	0·0	262	0·6	Tr.	0·2	0·4	0·03	0·01	1	7	1·1	5	
130	Liver, raw	4·7	2·3	0·0	41	24·4	92	2·4	5·9	3·95	1·65	89	68	28·4	67	
131	Liver, calf, fried ..	8·3	4·1	0·7	74	34·6	116	2·5	6·8	6·15	—	164	122	34·1	140	
132	Liver, ox, fried	8·4	4·5	1·1	81	26·1	110	2·4	7·5	5·89	—	156	116	23·3	133	
133	Meat paste	5·6	3·6	1·2	61	(267)	59	7·5	6·2	1·05	0·03	38	37	(426)	27	
134	Mutton chop, raw, lean only	5·3	3·4	0·0	53	25·9	100	3·6	7·7	0·48	0·05	55	59	23·8	34	
134*a*	Mutton chop, raw, lean only (weighed with fat and bone)	2·0	1·3	0·0	20	9·7	37	1·3	2·9	0·17	0·02	20	22	8·8	13	

135	Mutton chop, raw, lean and fat	3·9	14·9	0·0	154	21·3	70	3·6	5·3	0·28	0·05	49	42	19·8	30
135a	Mutton chop, raw, lean and fat (weighed with bone)	3·1	11·5	0·0	119	16·5	54	2·8	4·1	0·23	0·03	38	33	15·3	24
136	Mutton chop, grilled, lean only	7·5	5·0	0·0	77	36·0	114	5·9	8·5	0·71	0·05	68	81	31·2	48
136a	Mutton chop, grilled, lean only (weighed with fat and bone)	3·5	2·3	0·0	36	17·0	53	2·8	4·0	0·34	0·03	32	38	14·8	23
137	Mutton chop, grilled, lean and fat	5·7	12·8	0·0	142	29·0	87	5·1	6·5	0·68	0·05	58	60	25·5	40
137a	Mutton chop, grilled, lean and fat (weighed with bone)	4·3	9·7	0·0	108	21·8	65	3·8	4·9	0·51	0·04	44	46	19·3	30
138	Mutton chop, fried, lean only	6·5	7·2	1·6	97	33·0	99	4·4	7·4	0·88	0·04	63	71	38·0	47
138a	Mutton chop, fried, lean only (weighed with fat and bone)	2·4	2·7	0·6	36	12·5	37	1·6	2·8	0·34	0·01	24	27	14·2	18
139	Mutton chop, fried, lean and fat	4·4	17·1	0·7	178	24·4	69	4·0	5·1	0·74	0·03	52	47	26·1	36
139a	Mutton chop, fried, lean and fat (weighed with bone)	3·6	13·9	0·6	146	19·9	56	3·2	4·2	0·60	0·03	43	38	21·3	29
140	Mutton, leg, boiled ..	7·3	4·7	0·0	74	18·2	78	1·0	7·8	1·45	0·07	68	80	19·0	64
141	Mutton, leg, roast ..	7·1	5·8	0·0	83	20·1	98	1·2	7·5	1·22	—	69	77	17·6	57
142	Mutton, scrag and neck, stewed	6·9	6·9	0·0	92	18·8	53	14·2	7·6	1·93	—	63	74	23·3	57
142a	Mutton, scrag and neck, stewed (weighed with bone)	5·2	5·2	0·0	69	14·1	40	10·6	5·7	1·45	—	47	55	17·4	43
143	Partridge, roast	10·0	2·0	0·0	60	28·4	116	13·0	10·2	2·19	—	89	113	28·1	79
143a	Partridge, roast (weighed with bone)	6·0	1·2	0·0	36	17·0	69	7·8	6·1	1·31	—	53	68	16·8	47
144	Pheasant, roast	8·8	2·6	0·0	61	29·6	117	14·0	9·9	2·38	—	88	87	30·7	61
144a	Pheasant, roast (weighed with bone)	5·5	1·7	0·0	38	18·7	74	8·8	6·3	1·50	—	55	55	19·3	39
145	Pigeon, boiled	6·2	4·0	0·0	62	21·0	85	5·0	8·9	2·78	—	100	69	21·3	73
145a	Pigeon, boiled (weighed with bone)	2·7	1·7	0·0	27	9·2	37	2·2	3·9	1·22	—	44	30	9·4	32
146	Pigeon, roast	7·6	3·8	0·0	66	29·8	116	4·6	9·6	5·51	—	114	86	28·1	83
146a	Pigeon, roast (weighed with bone)	3·3	1·7	0·0	29	13·1	51	2·0	4·2	2·42	—	50	38	12·4	36

Meat, Poultry and Game—*continued*

No.	Food.	g. per oz.			Calories per oz.	mg. per oz.									Acid-base balance, c.c. per oz.	
		Protein.	Fat.	Carbohydrate (as glucose).		Na.	K.	Ca.	Mg.	Fe.	Cu.	P.	S.	Cl.	$\frac{N}{10}$ Acid.	$\frac{N}{10}$ Alkali.
147	Pork, leg, roast	7·0	6·6	0·0	90	18·8	88	1·5	6·4	0·48	—	103	72	23·6	81	
148	Pork, loin, roast, lean only	6·7	5·7	0·0	81	19·6	100	2·1	6·7	0·74	0·03	59	69	28·7	48	
149	Pork, loin, roast, lean and fat	5·5	11·5	0·0	129	17·0	82	2·1	5·1	0·65	0·03	53	57	21·8	42	
150	Pork, loin, salt, smoked, lean only	6·7	4·5	0·0	69	(511)	85	7·8	6·9	0·65	—	62	69	(880)	78	
151	Pork chops, grilled, lean only	7·2	6·7	0·0	92	21·6	99	2·6	5·9	0·82	0·03	60	74	32·1	53	
151*a*	Pork chops, grilled, lean only (weighed with bone)	3·0	2·8	0·0	38	8·8	40	1·1	2·4	0·34	0·01	25	30	13·2	22	
152	Pork chops, grilled, lean and fat	5·3	14·3	0·0	155	16·8	73	2·4	4·2	0·68	0·03	51	54	20·4	40	
152*a*	Pork chops, grilled, lean and fat (weighed with bone)	4·4	11·9	0·0	128	13·9	61	2·0	3·5	0·56	0·02	42	45	16·9	34	
153	Rabbit, stewed	7·6	2·2	0·0	51	9·1	60	3·2	6·1	0·54	0·06	57	70	12·2	57	
153*a*	Rabbit, stewed (weighed with bone)	3·9	1·1	0·0	26	4·6	30	1·6	3·1	0·28	0·03	29	36	6·2	29	
154	Sausage, beef, fried ..	3·9	5·2	4·5	81	(321)	72	6·0	4·7	1·16	0·05	48	46	(503)	37	
155	Sausage, pork, raw ..	2·5	8·2	2·8	97	(218)	45	4·3	3·3	0·72	0·03	31	21	(305)	7	
156	Sausage, pork, fried ..	3·3	7·1	3·6	93	(284)	58	5·6	4·2	0·94	0·04	40	27	(397)	10	
157	Sausage (1943), raw ..	3·0	4·6	4·1	70	(204)	73	(18)	12·5	0·68	0·09	55	—	(277)	—	—
158	Sausage (1943), grilled ..	4·1	5·7	5·5	90	(278)	99	(24)	17·0	0·91	0·11	75	—	(375)	—	—
159	Sausage, black	1·5	6·4	4·2	81	(255)	37	8·8	4·3	0·55	0·07	8	49	(374)	12	
160	Sausage, breakfast ..	2·5	5·8	4·8	82	(250)	48	6·2	4·7	0·54	0·02	24	22	(369)	6	
161	Suet	0·3	28·1	0·0	262	6·0	4	1·7	0·3	0·11	0·01	2	6	5·1	2	
162	Sweetbreads, stewed ..	6·4	2·6	0·0	51	19·6	66	4·1	4·4	0·46	—	169	53	21·0	117	
163	Tongue, ox, pickled ..	5·4	6·8	0·7	88	(532)	43	8·8	4·6	0·85	—	65	57	(851)	67	
164	Tongue, sheep's, stewed	5·1	6·8	0·0	84	22·5	31	3·2	3·7	0·97	—	56	53	22·7	53	
165	Tripe, stewed	5·1	0·9	0·0	29	20·4	3	(36)	2·2	0·45	—	38	41	8·5	23	
166	Turkey, roast	8·6	2·2	0·0	56	36·9	104	10·9	8·0	1·08	—	91	66	34·9	55	
166*a*	Turkey, roast (weighed with bone)	5·1	1·3	0·0	34	22·1	62	6·5	4·8	0·65	—	55	40	21·0	33	

No.	Food.	Protein.	Fat.	Carbohydrate (as glucose).	Calories per oz.	Na.	K.	Ca.	Mg.	Fe.	Cu.	P.	S.	Cl.	$\frac{N}{10}$ Acid.	$\frac{N}{10}$ Alkali.
167	Veal, fillet, raw	5·7	0·8	0·0	31	30·4	101	2·2	7·1	0·65	—	73	63	19·3	46	
168	Veal, frozen, raw ..	5·3	1·0	0·0	31	27·0	105	2·9	7·1	0·51	0·04	57	59	27·8	35	
169	Veal cutlet, fried ..	8·6	2·3	1·3	61	30·1	120	2·8	9·3	0·74	—	81	93	32·6	67	
170	Veal, fillet, roast ..	8·7	3·3	0·0	66	27·5	122	4·1	7·9	1·22	—	101	94	32·1	81	
171	Venison, roast	9·5	1·8	0·0	56	24·4	103	8·2	9·5	2·22	—	81	91	25·3	68	

Fish

No.	Food.	g. per oz.			Calories per oz.	mg. per oz.									Acid-base balance, c.c. per oz.	
		Protein.	Fat.	Carbohydrate (as glucose).		Na.	K.	Ca.	Mg.	Fe.	Cu.	P.	S.	Cl.	$\frac{N}{10}$ Acid.	$\frac{N}{10}$ Alkali.
172	Bass, steamed	5·5	1·5	0·0	36	21·3	93	13·3	7·6	0·20	—	62	66	24·1	42	
172a	Bass, steamed (weighed with bones)	2·9	0·8	0·0	19	11·3	49	7·1	4·0	0·11	—	33	35	12·8	22	
173	Bloaters, grilled ..	6·4	4·9	0·0	73	(200)	126	35·0	12·7	0·62	—	101	88	(322)	211	
173a	Bloaters, grilled (weighed with bones and skin)	4·7	3·7	0·0	54	(148)	94	25·9	9·4	0·46	—	75	65	(238)	156	
174	Bream, Red, steamed ..	5·6	1·1	0·0	34	33·8	98	7·9	8·5	0·11	—	61	69	39·2	42	
174a	Bream, Red, steamed (weighed with bones)	2·9	0·6	0·0	17	17·6	51	4·1	4·4	0·06	—	32	36	20·4	22	
175	Bream, Sea, steamed ..	5·1	0·9	0·0	29	32·1	80	9·9	7·6	0·17	—	68	62	34·6	47	
175a	Bream, Sea, steamed (weighed with bones)	3·3	0·6	0·0	19	20·8	52	6·4	4·9	0·11	—	44	40	22·4	30	
176	Brill, steamed	5·8	1·0	0·0	33	26·7	75	4·3	8·8	0·20	0·04	65	61	35·5	50	
176a	Brill, steamed (weighed with bones and skin)	3·9	0·7	0·0	22	18·2	51	2·9	6·0	0·14	0·03	45	42	24·1	34	
177	Catfish, steamed ..	5·8	1·1	0·0	34	30·6	90	3·9	7·6	0·17	—	60	61	30·6	41	
177a	Catfish, steamed (weighed with bones)	4·9	0·9	0·0	28	26·0	76	3·3	6·4	0·14	—	51	52	26·0	35	
178	Catfish, fried	5·3	3·0	1·8	57	34·0	92	5·4	7·3	0·65	—	65	57	42·5	42	
178a	Catfish, fried (weighed with bones)	5·0	2·8	1·7	53	32·0	86	5·1	6·9	0·61	—	61	53	40·0	39	

Fish—*continued*

No.	Food.	g. per oz.			Calories per oz.	mg. per oz.									Acid-base balance, c.c. per oz.	
		Protein.	Fat.	Carbohydrate (as glucose).		Na.	K.	Ca.	Mg.	Fe.	Cu.	P.	S.	Cl.	$\frac{N}{10}$ Acid.	$\frac{N}{10}$ Alkali.
179	Cockles	3·1	0·1	Tr.	14	(1000)	12	36·1	14·5	7·39	—	58	91	(1480)	44	
180	Cod, steamed	5·1	0·3	0·0	23	28·4	102	4·2	5·9	0·14	0·03	69	60	34·0	46	
180*a*	Cod, steamed (weighed with bones and skin)	4·1	0·2	0·0	19	23·0	83	3·4	4·7	0·11	0·02	56	49	27·5	37	
181	Cod, fried	5·9	1·3	0·8	40	45·8	97	14·1	7·6	0·28	0·03	74	69	41·1	44	
181*a*	Cod, fried (weighed with bones)	5·4	1·2	0·7	36	41·5	88	12·8	6·9	0·25	0·03	68	63	37·4	40	
182	Cod, grilled	7·7	1·5	0·0	45	31·2	116	8·8	10·2	0·28	—	78	92	36·9	62	
182*a*	Cod, grilled (weighed with bones and skin)	6·5	1·3	0·0	39	26·6	99	7·5	8·7	0·24	—	66	78	31·5	53	
183	Cod roe, fried	5·8	3·4	0·9	59	36·0	73	4·8	3·0	0·45	—	143	68	53·2	110	
184	Cod roe, baked in vinegar	6·8	0·9	0·0	34	20·7	38	3·7	2·3	0·65	—	114	77	49·1	114	
185	Conger, steamed ..	6·5	0·5	0·0	31	28·1	99	8·5	8·1	0·14	—	63	76	23·3	46	
185*a*	Conger, steamed (weighed with bones and skin)	4·9	0·4	0·0	23	21·0	74	6·4	6·1	0·11	—	47	57	17·5	35	
186	Conger, fried	5·3	5·7	1·8	81	30·6	100	6·9	8·3	0·28	—	70	63	44·3	48	
186*a*	Conger, fried (weighed with bones)	4·7	5·0	1·6	72	27·0	88	6·1	7·3	0·25	—	62	55	38·9	42	
187	Crab, boiled	5·4	1·5	0·0	36	104·0	77	8·3	13·6	0·37	—	99	132	162·0	112	
187*a*	Crab, boiled (weighed with shell)	1·1	0·3	0·0	7	20·7	15	1·7	2·7	0·07	—	20	26	32·4	22	
188	Dabs, fried	5·5	4·1	2·8	71	36·0	80	36·9	8·3	0·28	0·02	71	74	69·5	50	
188*a*	Dabs, fried (weighed with bones)	4·4	3·2	2·2	56	28·8	64	29·5	6·7	0·23	0·02	57	59	55·6	40	
189	Dogfish, fried	5·1	7·1	1·7	94	46·2	70	3·6	5·7	0·37	—	76	60	57·5	58	
189*a*	Dogfish, fried (weighed with bone)	4·6	6·5	1·6	85	42·0	63	3·2	5·2	0·34	—	69	54	52·2	53	
190	Eels, elvers, raw ..	3·6	0·6	0·0	20	19·0	65	146·5	8·8	1·14	Tr.	125	40	15·8	5	
191	Eels, silver, raw.. ..	4·1	7·9	0·0	90	21·8	61	3·6	4·1	0·23	0·01	55	46	19·7	39	
191*a*	Eels, silver, raw (weighed with bones and skin)	2·7	5·2	0·0	60	14·5	40	2·4	2·7	0·14	0·01	36	30	13·0	26	

192	Eels, silver, stewed ..	5·0	9·2	0·0	106	20·7	57	4·1	4·2	0·28	—	57	57	18·1	48
193	Eels, yellow, raw ..	4·7	3·2	0·0	49	25·3	76	5·3	5·4	0·20	0·01	63	53	16·2	41
193a	Eels, yellow, raw (weighed with bones and skin)	3·2	2·1	0·0	33	17·1	51	3·5	3·6	0·14	0·01	44	36	10·9	27
194	Fillet, smoked, steamed	5·5	0·3	0·0	25	(306)	76	5·6	12·4	0·28	—	63	71	(440)	42
195	Fish paste	4·2	2·7	1·9	49	(420)	87	41·5	8·6	1·70	0·02	60	53	(677)	29
196	Flounder, steamed ..	5·5	0·5	0·0	27	32·6	90	15·6	7·1	0·37	—	84	66	42·0	56
196a	Flounder, steamed (weighed with bones and skin)	3·1	0·3	0·0	15	18·2	50	8·8	4·0	0·21	—	47	37	23·5	31
197	Flounder, fried	4·8	3·7	1·8	61	36·9	80	21·1	6·4	0·31	—	62	58	56·8	40
197a	Flounder, fried (weighed with bones)	3·3	2·5	1·3	42	25·5	55	14·6	4·4	0·22	—	43	40	39·1	27
198	Gurnet, grey, steamed ..	6·0	1·5	0·0	38	33·2	87	3·7	6·8	0·23	—	56	70	33·2	45
198a	Gurnet, grey, steamed (weighed with bones and skin)	4·8	1·2	0·0	31	26·9	70	3·0	5·5	0·18	—	45	57	26·9	36
199	Gurnet, red, steamed ..	6·0	1·3	0·0	37	52·9	99	5·9	8·8	0·20	—	68	72	40·0	42
199a	Gurnet, red, steamed (weighed with bones and skin)	4·3	0·9	0·0	26	37·5	70	4·2	6·2	0·14	—	49	51	28·4	30
200	Haddock, fillets, raw ..	4·5	0·2	0·0	20	35·5	86	9·0	6·4	0·28	—	61	63	44·3	44
201	Haddock, fresh, steamed	6·2	0·2	0·0	28	34·4	92	15·5	7·9	0·20	0·04	66	86	22·1	50
201a	Haddock, fresh, steamed (weighed with bones and skin)	4·7	0·2	0·0	21	26·2	70	11·8	6·0	0·15	0·03	51	66	16·8	38
202	Haddock, fresh, fried ..	5·8	2·4	1·0	50	50·2	99	32·4	8·7	0·34	—	70	81	51·3	40
202a	Haddock, fresh, fried (weighed with bones)	5·3	2·2	0·9	46	46·3	91	29·8	8·0	0·31	—	64	75	47·1	37
203	Haddock, smoked, steamed	6·3	0·3	0·0	28	(346)	83	16·3	7·2	0·28	—	71	72	(540)	56
203a	Haddock, smoked, steamed (weighed with bones and skin)	4·1	0·2	0·0	18	(225)	54	10·6	4·7	0·18	—	46	47	(350)	36
204	Hake, steamed	5·2	0·9	0·0	30	33·5	88	4·5	7·6	0·17	0·03	62	55	27·0	36
204a	Hake, steamed (weighed with bones and skin)	4·2	0·7	0·0	24	26·8	70	3·6	6·1	0·14	0·03	50	44	21·6	29
205	Hake, fried	5·5	3·2	1·5	58	43·5	84	7·3	8·2	0·26	0·05	74	56	38·0	42
205a	Hake, fried (weighed with bones)	5·2	3·0	1·4	55	40·8	79	6·9	7·7	0·24	0·05	69	53	35·7	39

Fish—*continued*

No.	Food.	g. per oz.			Calories per oz.	mg. per oz.									Acid-base balance, c.c. per oz.	
		Protein.	Fat.	Carbohydrate (as glucose).		Na.	K.	Ca.	Mg.	Fe.	Cu.	P.	S.	Cl.	$\frac{N}{10}$ Acid.	$\frac{N}{10}$ Alkali.
206	Halibut, steamed ..	6·4	1·1	0·0	37	31·5	97	3·7	6·6	0·17	0·02	72	72	22·7	53	
206*a*	Halibut, steamed (weighed with bones and skin)	4·9	0·8	0·0	28	23·8	74	2·8	5·0	0·13	0·01	55	54	17·3	40	
207	Herring, raw	4·7	5·1	0·0	67	36·9	90	28·7	9·0	0·43	—	77	54	34·6	33	
208	Herring, fried in oatmeal	6·2	4·3	0·4	67	28·7	118	11·0	9·9	0·54	—	96	74	35·5	62	
208*a*	Herring, fried in oatmeal (weighed with bones)	5·4	3·8	0·4	59	25·2	104	9·7	8·7	0·48	—	85	65	31·2	55	
209	Herring, baked in vinegar	4·8	3·7	0·0	54	17·6	66	16·6	6·2	0·45	—	93	58	33·7	68	
209*a*	Herring, baked in vinegar (weighed with bones)	4·4	3·4	0·0	50	16·2	61	15·2	5·7	0·42	—	85	53	31·0	62	
210	Herring roe, fried ..	6·6	4·5	1·3	74	24·6	68	4·5	2·3	0·43	—	260	69	34·9	188	
211	John Dory, steamed ..	5·6	0·4	0·0	27	39·5	81	6·5	8·2	0·17	—	71	67	40·5	51	
211*a*	John Dory, steamed (weighed with bones and skin)	3·5	0·2	0·0	17	24·4	50	4·0	5·1	0·11	—	44	41	25·2	32	
212	Kippers, baked	6·6	3·2	0·0	57	(281)	148	18·4	13·5	0·40	—	121	80	(433)	69	
212*a*	Kippers, baked (weighed with bones and skin)	3·6	1·7	0·0	31	(152)	80	9·9	7·3	0·22	—	65	43	(234)	38	
213	Lemon sole, steamed ..	5·6	0·3	0·0	26	32·6	79	6·3	5·7	0·17	0·03	70	69	33·2	34	
213*a*	Lemon sole, steamed (weighed with bones and skin)	4·0	0·2	0·0	18	23·2	56	4·5	4·0	0·12	0·03	50	49	23·5	24	
214	Lemon sole, fried ..	4·4	3·7	2·6	62	38·6	71	26·9	5·1	0·31	0·05	68	54	35·2	35	
214*a*	Lemon sole, fried (weighed with bones)	3·5	2·9	2·1	49	30·5	56	21·3	4·0	0·25	0·04	54	42	27·8	28	
215	Ling, steamed	6·4	0·2	0·0	28	34·0	105	5·0	10·4	0·14	—	63	76	28·1	42	
215*a*	Ling, steamed (weighed with bones and skin)	4·8	0·2	0·0	21	25·5	79	3·8	7·9	0·11	—	47	57	21·0	32	
216	Ling, fried	4·8	3·5	1·8	59	41·1	89	11·3	9·1	0·23	—	65	58	44·5	36	
216*a*	Ling, fried (weighed with bones)	4·3	3·1	1·6	52	36·6	79	10·0	8·1	0·20	—	58	51	39·6	32	

217	Lobster, boiled	6·0	1·0	0·0	34	92·3	73	17·5	9·7	0·23	—	81	146	149·0	109
217*a*	Lobster, boiled (weighed with shell)	2·2	0·3	0·0	12	33·2	26	6·3	3·5	0·09	—	29	53	53·6	39
218	Mackerel, fried	5·7	3·2	0·0	53	43·5	118	8·1	9·9	0·34	0·06	80	60	32·4	36
218*a*	Mackerel, fried (weighed with bones and skin)	4·2	2·3	0·0	39	31·8	86	5·9	7·2	0·25	0·04	58	44	23·6	26
219	Megrim, raw	4·9	0·3	0·0	22	34·4	76	17·5	8·3	0·34	—	53	58	34·6	30
220	Megrim, steamed ..	5·9	0·4	0·0	28	27·2	61	21·6	7·9	0·26	—	62	70	33·8	49
220*a*	Megrim, steamed (weighed with bones and skin)	3·9	0·3	0·0	18	18·2	41	14·4	5·3	0·17	—	41	47	22·7	33
221	Megrim, fried	5·5	3·3	2·7	64	50·1	71	17·8	8·8	0·17	—	62	67	52·0	40
221*a*	Megrim, fried (weighed with bones)	4·7	2·8	2·3	54	42·6	61	15·2	7·5	0·14	—	53	57	44·3	34
222	Monkfish, steamed ..	6·2	0·3	0·0	28	38·3	101	3·0	8·4	0·14	—	61	73	38·6	45
222*a*	Monkfish, steamed (weighed with bones)	5·0	0·2	0·0	23	31·0	82	2·4	6·8	0·11	—	49	59	31·2	36
223	Monkfish, fried	4·8	2·3	1·7	48	46·5	114	3·2	9·0	0·34	—	58	58	55·9	32
223*a*	Monkfish, fried (weighed with bones)	4·1	2·0	1·5	41	40·0	98	2·8	7·7	0·29	—	50	50	48·0	27
224	Mullet, grey, steamed ..	6·1	1·1	0·0	36	26·6	78	4·0	8·5	0·57	—	73	72	21·8	57
224*a*	Mullet, grey, steamed (weighed with bones and skin)	3·9	0·7	0·0	23	17·0	50	2·6	5·4	0·37	—	47	46	14·0	36
225	Mullet, red, steamed ..	6·1	1·2	0·0	36	33·5	103	8·3	9·3	0·26	—	80	73	28·6	53
225*a*	Mullet, red, steamed (weighed with bones)	4·0	0·8	0·0	24	22·1	68	5·5	6·2	0·17	—	53	49	19·0	35
226	Mussels, raw	3·3	0·5	Tr.	19	82·0	90	25·0	6·5	1·65	—	67	104	131·0	69
227	Mussels, boiled	4·8	0·6	Tr.	25	59·8	26	56·0	7·1	3·84	—	94	99	89·5	81
227*a*	Mussels, boiled (weighed with shells)	1·4	0·2	Tr.	7	17·9	8	16·8	2·1	1·16	—	28	30	36·8	24
228	Oysters, raw	2·9	0·3	Tr.	14	143·0	73	52·9	11·9	1·70	—	76	71	231·0	41
228*a*	Oysters, raw (weighed with shells)	0·3	Tr.	Tr.	2	17·2	9	6·3	1·4	0·20	—	9	9	27·8	5
229	Pilchards, tinned (fish only)	6·2	3·1	0·0	54	(169)	87	65·8	11·8	0·88	0·06	84	70	(257)	35
230	Pilchards, tinned (whole contents of tin)	5·4	4·4	0·0	63	(163)	82	54·0	10·8	0·74	0·05	77	60	(247)	28
231	Plaice, raw	4·3	0·5	0·0	22	27·2	100	4·7	6·2	0·23	—	62	61	23·6	40
232	Plaice, steamed	5·1	0·5	0·0	26	34·0	79	10·7	6·8	0·17	—	70	71	31·8	52
232*a*	Plaice, steamed (weighed with bones and skin)	2·8	0·3	0·0	14	18·4	43	5·8	3·7	0·09	—	38	38	17·2	28

Fish—*continued*

No.	Food.	g. per oz.			Calories per oz.	mg. per oz.									Acid-base balance c.c. per oz.	
		Protein.	Fat.	Carbohydrate (as glucose).		Na.	K.	Ca.	Mg.	Fe.	Cu.	P.	S.	Cl.	$\frac{N}{10}$ Acid.	$\frac{N}{10}$ Alkali.
233	Plaice, fried	5·1	4·1	2·0	66	35·3	62	12·7	6·9	0·23	0·04	71	71	49·4	61	
233a	Plaice, fried (weighed with bones)	3·1	2·5	1·2	40	21·5	38	7·8	4·2	0·14	0·03	43	43	30·1	37	
234	Pollack, steamed ..	5·5	0·2	0·0	25	27·0	124	3·6	9·3	0·14	—	57	68	32·4	35	
234a	Pollack, steamed (weighed with bones and skin)	4·8	0·2	0·0	21	23·2	107	3·1	8·0	0·12	—	49	58	27·8	30	
235	Pollack, fried	4·7	2·0	1·9	45	46·0	95	36·4	12·9	0·79	—	69	56	78·1	28	
235a	Pollack, fried (weighed with bones)	4·3	1·8	1·7	41	42·3	87	33·5	11·8	0·73	—	63	52	72·0	26	
236	Pollan, steamed ..	5·1	0·6	0·0	27	19·6	106	23·3	6·5	0·26	—	82	63	20·2	45	
236a	Pollan, steamed (weighed with bones and skin)	3·1	0·4	0·0	16	11·9	65	14·2	4·0	0·16	—	50	38	12·3	27	
237	Pollan, fried	5·3	3·5	0·5	56	18·2	111	56·8	7·4	0·34	—	104	65	18·2	42	
237a	Pollan, fried (weighed with bones)	3·8	2·5	0·3	40	13·1	80	40·8	5·3	0·25	—	75	47	13·1	30	
238	Prawns	6·0	0·5	0·0	30	(451)	74	41·2	11·9	0·31	—	99	104	(725)	87	
238a	Prawns (weighed with shells)	2·3	0·2	0·0	11	(172)	28	15·6	4·5	0·12	—	38	40	(275)	33	
239	Saithe, steamed	6·4	0·2	0·0	28	27·5	99	5·3	8·8	0·17	—	71	76	23·6	52	
239a	Saithe, steamed (weighed with bones and skin)	5·4	0·1	0·0	24	23·5	84	4·5	7·5	0·14	—	61	64	20·1	44	
240	Salmon, fresh, steamed	5·4	3·7	0·0	57	30·4	95	8·2	8·1	0·23	—	86	54	18·2	46	
240a	Salmon, fresh, steamed (weighed with bones and skin)	4·4	3·0	0·0	46	24·7	77	6·6	6·6	0·18	—	70	44	14·8	37	
241	Salmon, tinned	5·6	1·7	0·0	39	(152)	91	18·8	8·5	0·37	0·01	81	67	(246)	57	
242	Sardines, tinned ..	5·8	6·4	0·0	84	(223)	123	116·0	11·7	1·13	0·01	194	80	(342)	75	
243	Scallops, steamed ..	6·4	0·4	Tr.	30	75·3	135	32·7	10·9	0·85	—	96	162	116·0	103	
244	Shrimps	6·3	0·7	0·0	32	(1090)	114	91·0	29·8	0·51	0·23	77	96	(1660)	5	
244a	Shrimps (weighed with shells)	2·1	0·2	0·0	11	(360)	38	30·0	9·8	0·17	0·08	25	32	(550)	2	

245	Skate, fried	4·3	4·7	2·1	69	51·8	67	5·5	6·6	0·34	—	68	61	75·7	55	
245a	Skate, fried (weighed with bones)	3·5	3·9	1·8	57	42·9	56	4·6	5·5	0·28	—	56	50	62·8	46	
246	Smelts, fried	7·1	8·8	1·4	116	42·0	147	195·0	16·6	0·94	—	152	86	39·2		11
246a	Smelts, fried (weighed with heads)	6·0	7·5	1·2	98	35·7	124	166·0	14·2	0·80	—	129	73	33·3		9
247	Sole, steamed	5·0	0·4	0·0	24	31·2	68	32·1	8·0	0·20	—	77	67	37·5	48	
247a	Sole, steamed (weighed with bones and skin)	3·0	0·2	0·0	14	18·7	41	19·3	4·8	0·12	—	46	40	22·5	29	
248	Sole, fried	5·7	5·2	1·5	78	54·5	67	37·2	7·9	0·40	—	74	75	54·9	44	
248a	Sole, fried (weighed with bones)	5·0	4·6	1·3	68	48·0	59	32·7	7·0	0·15	—	65	66	48·3	39	
249	Sprats, fresh, fried ..	6·3	10·8	0·0	126	37·5	116	201·0	13·0	1·28	—	180	81	51·6	24	
249a	Sprats, fresh, fried (weighed with heads)	5·6	9·5	0·0	111	33·0	102	176·0	11·4	1·12	—	158	71	45·4	21	
250	Sprats, smoked, grilled ..	7·1	6·6	0·0	91	(240)	137	124·0	11·4	1·62	—	161	78	(378)	48	
250a	Sprats, smoked, grilled (weighed with heads)	6·3	5·9	0·0	81	(213)	122	110·0	10·1	1·44	—	143	70	(336)	43	
251	Stockfish, boiled ..	9·1	0·3	0·0	40	(112)	9	6·4	9·9	0·51	—	46	106	(190)	87	
251a	Stockfish, boiled (weighed with bones and skin)	7·6	0·2	0·0	33	(93)	7	5·3	8·2	0·42	—	38	88	(158)	72	
252	Sturgeon, steamed ..	7·0	1·6	0·0	44	30·6	67	4·3	5·3	0·57	—	75	83	39·2	74	
252a	Sturgeon, steamed (weighed with bone)	4·8	1·1	0·0	30	20·8	46	2·9	3·6	0·39	—	51	56	26·6	50	
253	Torsk, steamed	6·4	0·2	0·0	28	21·0	110	7·7	7·5	0·28	—	80	79	28·7	62	
253a	Torsk, steamed (weighed with bones and skin)	3·8	0·1	0·0	16	12·4	65	4·5	4·4	0·17	—	47	47	16·9	37	
254	Torsk, fried	5·5	1·2	2·2	42	26·4	106	18·4	7·1	0·17	—	85	67	43·5	55	
254a	Torsk, fried (weighed with bones and skin)	3·9	0·9	1·6	30	18·8	75	13·0	5·0	0·12	—	60	47	30·9	39	
255	Trout, steamed	6·3	1·3	0·0	38	25·0	106	10·2	8·8	0·28	—	77	62	19·9	43	
255a	Trout, steamed (weighed with bones and skin)	4·2	0·9	0·0	25	16·5	70	6·7	5·8	0·19	—	51	41	13·1	28	
256	Trout, Sea, steamed ..	6·0	1·4	0·0	37	58·7	89	3·5	8·6	0·28	—	82	74	74·1	63	
256a	Trout, Sea, steamed (weighed with bones and skin)	4·7	1·1	0·0	29	46·3	70	2·8	6·8	0·22	—	65	58	58·6	49	

Fish—*continued*

No.	Food.	g. per oz.			Calories per oz.	mg. per oz.									Acid-base balance, c.c. per oz.	
		Protein.	Fat.	Carbohydrate (as glucose).		Na.	K.	Ca.	Mg.	Fe.	Cu.	P.	S.	Cl.	$\frac{N}{10}$ Acid.	$\frac{N}{10}$ Alkali.
257	Turbot, steamed ..	5·9	0·5	0·0	28	25·6	72	3·8	6·8	0·14	—	53	70	40·3	52	
257a	Turbot, steamed (weighed with bones and skin)	3·9	0·3	0·0	19	16·9	48	2·5	4·5	0·09	—	35	46	26·6	34	
258	Whelks	5·1	0·5	Tr.	26	(75)	90	15·3	45·4	1·76	—	64	127	(166)	66	
258a	Whelks (weighed with shells)	0·8	0·1	Tr.	4	(11)	13	2·3	6·8	0·26	—	10	19	(25)	10	
259	Whitebait, fried ..	5·2	13·5	1·5	152	63·9	32	244·0	14·3	1·45	—	243	77	92·3	61	
260	Whiting, steamed ..	5·7	0·3	0·0	26	36·1	85	11·9	8·0	0·28	—	54	87	26·4	46	
260a	Whiting, steamed (weighed with bones and skin)	3·8	0·2	0·0	17	24·5	58	8·1	5·4	0·19	—	36	59	17·9	32	
261	Whiting, fried	4·9	2·9	2·0	55	56·5	90	13·6	9·2	0·20	—	73	76	55·1	48	
261a	Whiting, fried (weighed with bones and skin)	4·4	2·6	1·8	49	50·9	81	12·2	8·3	0·18	—	66	68	49·7	43	
262	Winkles, boiled in salt water	4·3	0·4	Tr.	21	(325)	44	38·7	102·0	4·26	—	62	107	(511)		6
262a	Winkles, boiled in salt water (weighed with shells)	0·8	0·1	Tr.	4	(62)	8	7·3	19·3	0·81	—	12	20	(97)		1
263	Winkles, boiled in fresh water	5·0	0·7	Tr.	27	75·8	60	46·9	118·0	4·86	—	79	127	142·0	<1	
263a	Winkles, boiled in fresh water (weighed with shells)	0·7	0·1	Tr.	4	11·4	9	7·0	17·6	0·73	—	12	19	21·3	<1	
264	Witch, steamed	5·4	0·3	0·0	25	38·6	86	8·6	6·8	0·26	—	66	72	34·9	48	
264a	Witch, steamed (weighed with bones and skin)	3·2	0·2	0·0	15	23·2	52	5·2	4·1	0·15	—	40	43	20·9	29	
265	Witch, fried	5·0	4·0	2·2	66	50·0	85	14·8	6·9	0·23	—	53	67	53·1	34	
265a	Witch, fried (weighed with bones and skin)	4·2	3·4	1·9	56	42·0	71	12·4	5·8	0·19	—	45	56	44·5	29	

Fruit

No.	Food.	g. per oz.			Calories per oz.	mg. per oz.									Acid-base balance, c.c. per oz.	
		Protein (N× 6·25).	Fat.	Available carbohydrate (as monosaccharides).		Na.	K.	Ca.	Mg.	Fe.	Cu.	P.	S.	Cl.	$\frac{N}{10}$ Acid.	$\frac{N}{10}$ Alkali.
266	Apples, Empire eating ..	0·1	Tr.	3·5	13	0·8	33	1·0	1·4	0·08	0·04	1·9	1·1	Tr.		9
266a	Apples, Empire eating (weighed with skin and core)	0·1	Tr.	2·6	10	0·6	25	0·8	1·1	0·06	0·03	1·4	0·8	Tr.		7
267	Apples, English eating ..	0·1	Tr.	3·3	13	0·6	34	1·0	1·2	0·08	0·02	2·4	2·2	0·6		7
267a	Apples, English eating (weighed with skin and core)	0·1	Tr.	2·6	10	0·5	27	0·8	1·0	0·07	0·02	1·9	1·7	0·5		6
268	Apples, cooking, raw ..	0·1	Tr.	2·7	10	0·6	35	1·0	0·8	0·08	0·03	4·6	0·8	1·3		7
269	Apples, cooking, baked ..	0·1	Tr.	2·8	11	0·6	36	1·0	0·9	0·09	0·03	4·8	0·9	1·4		7
269a	Apples, cooking, baked (weighed with skin)	0·1	Tr.	2·3	9	0·5	29	0·8	0·7	0·07	0·02	3·8	0·7	1·1		5
270	Apples, cooking, stewed without sugar	Tr.	Tr.	1·2	5	0·3	16	0·5	0·4	0·04	0·01	2·1	0·4	0·6		3
271	Apricots, fresh	0·2	Tr.	1·9	8	Tr.	91	4·9	3·5	0·11	0·03	6·1	1·7	Tr.		24
271a	Apricots, fresh (weighed with stones)	0·2	Tr.	1·7	7	Tr.	84	4·5	3·2	0·10	0·03	5·6	1·6	Tr.		22
272	Apricots, dried, raw ..	1·4	Tr.	12·3	52	16·0	535	26·3	18·6	1·16	0·08	33·5	46·6	9·8		119
273	Apricots, dried (stewed without sugar)	0·6	Tr.	5·1	21	6·7	223	10·9	7·7	0·48	0·03	13·9	19·4	4·1		49
274	Apricots, tinned in syrup	0·1	Tr.	4·5	17	0·3	73	3·4	2·0	0·20	0·01	3·7	0·3	0·4		20
275	Avocado pears	0·3	2·3	0·7	25	4·6	112	4·4	8·3	0·15	0·06	8·8	5·5	1·7		30
276	Bananas	0·3	Tr.	5·5	22	0·3	99	1·9	11·9	0·12	0·05	8·0	3·7	22·3		23
276a	Bananas (weighed with skin)	0·2	Tr.	3·2	13	0·2	58	1·1	7·0	0·07	0·03	4·7	2·2	13·1		13
277	Blackberries, raw ..	0·4	Tr.	1·8	8	1·1	59	18·0	8·4	0·24	0·03	6·8	2·6	6·3		24
278	Blackberries, stewed without sugar	0·2	Tr.	0·9	4	0·5	30	9·1	4·2	0·12	0·02	3·4	1·3	3·2		12

Fruit—*continued*

No.	Food.	g. per oz. Protein (N × 6·25).	Fat.	Available carbohydrate (as monosaccharides.)	Calories per oz.	mg. per oz. Na.	K.	Ca.	Mg.	Fe.	Cu.	P.	S.	Cl.	Acid-base balance c.c. per oz. $\frac{N}{10}$ Acid.	$\frac{N}{10}$ Alkali.
279	Cherries, eating	0·2	Tr.	3·4	13	0·8	78	4·5	2·7	0·11	0·02	4·8	1·9	Tr.		21
279*a*	Cherries, eating (weighed with stones)	0·1	Tr.	3·0	11	0·7	68	3·9	2·4	0·09	0·02	4·2	1·7	Tr.		18
280	Cherries, cooking, raw ..	0·2	Tr.	3·3	13	1·2	87	5·7	3·3	0·09	0·03	5·9	2·2	Tr.		23
280*a*	Cherries, cooking, raw (weighed with stones)	0·1	Tr.	2·8	11	1·0	73	4·8	2·8	0·07	0·02	5·0	1·9	Tr.		19
281	Cherries, stewed without sugar (weighed with stones)	0·1	Tr.	1·2	5	0·4	31	2·0	1·2	0·03	0·01	2·1	0·8	Tr.		8
282	Cranberries	0·1	Tr.	1·0	4	0·5	34	4·2	2·4	0·32	0·04	3·2	3·2	Tr.		9
283	Currants, black, raw ..	0·3	Tr.	1·9	8	0·8	106	17·2	4·9	0·36	0·04	12·3	9·4	4·2		25
284	Currants, black, stewed without sugar	0·2	Tr.	1·3	6	0·5	74	12·0	3·4	0·25	0·03	8·6	6·6	2·9		17
285	Currants, red, raw ..	0·3	Tr.	1·2	6	0·7	78	10·2	3·6	0·35	0·03	8·4	8·1	4·0		17
286	Currants, red, stewed without sugar	0·2	Tr.	0·9	5	0·5	57	7·4	2·6	0·25	0·02	6·1	5·9	2·9		12
287	Currants, white	0·4	Tr.	1·6	7	0·4	83	6·4	3·6	0·26	0·04	8·0	6·7	3·0		17
288	Currants, dried	0·5	Tr.	18·0	69	5·5	201	27·1	10·3	0·52	0·14	11·4	8·8	4·5		62
289	Custard apple	0·6	Tr.	5·1	22	3·9	164	3·4	6·8	0·15	0·04	14·5	7·6	11·4		34
290	Damsons, raw	0·1	Tr.	2·7	11	0·6	82	6·7	3·1	0·12	0·02	4·7	1·8	Tr.		23
290*a*	Damsons, raw (weighed with stones)	0·1	Tr.	2·4	9	0·6	74	6·0	2·8	0·11	0·02	4·2	1·6	Tr.		21
291	Damsons, stewed without sugar (weighed with stones)	0·1	Tr.	1·8	7	0·4	56	4·6	2·2	0·08	0·02	3·2	1·2	Tr.		16
292	Dates	0·6	Tr.	18·1	70	1·4	215	19·2	16·6	0·46	0·06	18·1	14·5	82·4		36
292*a*	Dates (weighed with stones)	0·5	Tr.	15·6	61	1·2	185	16·6	14·3	0·39	0·05	15·6	12·4	71·0		30

293	Figs, green	0·4	Tr.	2·7	12	0·5	76	9·7	5·7	0·12	0·02	9·1	3·7	5·2		20
294	Figs, dried, raw	1·0	Tr.	15·0	61	24·6	288	80·5	26·2	1·18	0·07	26·0	22·9	47·1		102
295	Figs, dried, stewed without sugar	0·6	Tr.	8·5	35	14·0	164	45·8	14·9	0·67	0·04	14·8	13·0	26·8		58
296	Fruit salad, tinned in syrup	0·1	Tr.	5·3	20	0·7	33	2·4	2·2	0·98	0·01	2·7	0·5	0·9		9
297	Gooseberries, green, raw	0·3	Tr.	1·0	5	0·5	60	8·0	2·0	0·09	0·04	9·6	4·5	1·9		12
298	Gooseberries, green, stewed without sugar	0·2	Tr.	0·5	3	0·3	30	4·0	1·0	0·05	0·02	4·8	2·3	1·0		6
299	Gooseberries, ripe ..	0·2	Tr.	2·6	10	0·3	48	5·2	2·4	0·16	0·04	5·4	3·8	3·0		10
300	Grapes, black	0·2	Tr.	4·4	17	0·5	90	1·2	1·1	0·10	0·02	4·6	2·1	Tr.		20
300*a*	Grapes, black (whole grapes weighed)	0·1	Tr.	3·7	14	0·4	75	1·0	1·0	0·08	0·02	3·8	1·8	Tr.		17
301	Grapes, white	0·2	Tr.	4·6	18	0·5	71	5·4	1·9	0·10	0·03	6·2	2·6	Tr.		17
301*a*	Grapes, white (whole grapes weighed)	0·2	Tr.	4·4	17	0·4	67	5·2	1·8	0·09	0·03	5·9	2·5	Tr.		16
302	Grapefruit	0·2	Tr.	1·5	6	0·4	66	4·9	3·0	0·07	0·02	4·4	1·5	0·4		18
302*a*	Grapefruit (whole fruit weighed)	0·1	Tr.	0·7	3	0·2	32	2·3	1·4	0·04	0·01	2·1	0·7	0·2		9
303	Greengages	0·2	Tr.	3·4	14	0·4	87	4·8	2·2	0·11	0·02	6·4	0·9	0·3		22
303*a*	Greengages (weighed with stones)	0·2	Tr.	3·2	13	0·4	82	4·5	2·1	0·10	0·02	6·1	0·8	0·3		21
304	Greengages, stewed without sugar (weighed with stones)	0·1	Tr.	2·2	9	0·3	56	3·1	1·4	0·07	0·01	4·1	0·5	0·2		14
305	Lemons, whole	0·2	Tr.	0·9	4	1·7	46	30·5	3·3	0·10	0·07	5·9	3·5	1·5		24
306	Lemon juice	0·1	Tr.	0·5	2	0·4	40	2·4	1·9	0·04	0·04	2·9	0·6	0·7		11
307	Loganberries	0·3	Tr.	1·0	5	0·7	73	10·0	7·1	0·39	0·04	6·9	5·1	4·5		21
308	Loganberries, tinned in syrup	0·2	Tr.	7·4	29	0·3	28	5·0	3·2	0·82	0·01	6·5	0·9	1·3		7
309	Medlars	0·1	Tr.	3·0	12	1·7	70	8·6	3·0	0·14	0·05	8·0	4·7	0·9		17
309*a*	Medlars (weighed with skin and stone)	0·1	Tr.	2·4	10	1·4	57	6·9	2·4	0·11	0·04	6·5	3·8	0·7		14
310	Melons, Cantaloupe ..	0·3	Tr.	1·5	7	3·8	90	5·4	5·7	0·23	0·01	8·6	3·3	12·4		21
310*a*	Melons, Cantaloupe (weighed with skin)	0·2	Tr.	0·9	4	2·4	57	3·4	3·6	0·14	0·01	5·4	2·1	7·7		13
311	Melons, yellow	0·2	Tr.	1·4	6	5·5	63	3·9	3·8	0·07	0·01	2·5	1·8	12·8		17
311*a*	Melons, yellow (weighed with skin)	0·1	Tr.	0·9	4	3·5	39	2·4	2·4	0·04	0·01	1·5	1·1	8·0		11

Fruit—*continued*

No.	Food.	g. per oz.			Calories per oz.	mg. per oz.									Acid-base balance, c.c. per oz.	
		Protein (N × 6·25).	Fat.	Available carbohydrate (as monosaccharides).		Na.	K.	Ca.	Mg.	Fe.	Cu.	P.	S.	Cl.	$\frac{N}{10}$ Acid.	$\frac{N}{10}$ Alkali.
312	Mulberries	0·4	Tr.	2·3	10	0·6	73	10·2	4·3	0·45	0·02	13·5	2·5	1·1		17
313	Nectarines	0·3	Tr.	3·5	14	2·6	76	1·1	3·6	0·13	0·02	6·8	2·8	1·3		18
313*a*	Nectarines (weighed with stones)	0·2	Tr.	3·2	13	2·4	70	1·0	3·3	0·12	0·02	6·3	2·6	1·2		16
314	Olives (in brine) ..	0·3	3·1	0·0	30	(639)	26	17·4	6·2	0·29	0·07	4·8	10·1	(1060)	11	
314*a*	Olives (in brine) (weighed with stones)	0·2	2·5	0·0	24	(510)	21	14·0	5·0	0·23	0·05	3·8	8·1	(855)	9	
315	Oranges	0·2	Tr.	2·4	10	0·8	56	11·7	3·7	0·09	0·02	6·7	2·6	0·9		17
315*a*	Oranges (weighed with peel and pips)	0·2	Tr.	1·8	8	0·6	42	8·8	2·8	0·07	0·01	5·1	1·9	0·7		13
316	Orange juice	0·2	Tr.	2·7	11	0·5	51	3·3	3·3	0·09	0·01	6·2	1·3	0·3		13
317	Passion fruit	0·8	Tr.	1·8	10	8·1	99	4·4	11·0	0·32	0·03	15·4	5·3	10·4		24
317*a*	Passion fruit (weighed with skin)	0·3	Tr.	0·7	4	3·4	42	1·8	4·6	0·13	0·01	6·5	2·2	4·4		10
318	Peaches, fresh	0·2	Tr.	2·6	11	0·8	74	1·4	2·3	0·11	0·01	5·3	1·6	Tr.		17
318*a*	Peaches, fresh (weighed with stones)	0·2	Tr.	2·3	9	0·7	64	1·2	2·0	0·09	0·01	4·6	1·4	Tr.		15
319	Peaches, dried, raw ..	1·0	Tr.	15·0	61	1·7	314	10·1	15·4	1·92	0·18	33·0	68·1	3·0		34
320	Peaches, dried, stewed without sugar	0·3	Tr.	5·1	20	0·6	107	3·4	5·2	0·65	0·06	11·2	23·2	1·0		12
321	Peaches, tinned in syrup	0·1	Tr.	4·9	19	0·4	43	1·0	1·8	0·55	0·02	2·8	0·3	1·2		11
322	Pears, Empire eating ..	0·1	Tr.	3·1	12	0·7	37	2·3	2·6	0·05	0·06	2·8	1·6	Tr.		10
322*a*	Pears, Empire eating (weighed with skin and core)	0·1	Tr.	2·1	8	0·5	25	1·6	1·8	0·04	0·04	1·9	1·1	Tr.		7
323	Pears, English eating ..	0·1	Tr.	3·0	11	0·7	36	2·0	1·5	0·06	0·03	2·7	0·8	Tr.		10
323*a*	Pears, English eating (weighed with skin and core)	0·1	Tr.	2·2	9	0·5	27	1·5	1·1	0·05	0·02	2·0	0·6	Tr.		7

324	Pears, cooking, raw ..	0·1	Tr.	2·6	10	0·7	28	2·0	1·2	0·05	0·03	4·2	1·0	0·4		6
325	Pears, cooking (stewed without sugar)	0·1	Tr.	1·8	7	0·5	20	1·4	0·8	0·03	0·02	2·9	0·7	0·3		4
326	Pears, tinned in syrup ..	0·1	Tr.	4·7	18	0·4	26	1·5	1·7	0·50	0·01	1·5	0·4	0·8		7
327	Pineapple, fresh.. ..	0·1	Tr.	3·3	13	0·5	70	3·5	4·8	0·12	0·02	2·2	0·7	8·1		20
328	Pineapple, tinned in syrup	0·1	Tr.	4·7	18	0·1	16	3·8	2·3	0·48	0·01	1·4	0·8	1·2		6
329	Plums, Victoria dessert	0·2	Tr.	2·7	11	0·5	53	3·1	2·0	0·10	0·03	4·6	1·0	Tr.		14
329*a*	Plums, Victoria dessert (weighed with stones)	0·2	Tr.	2·6	10	0·5	50	2·9	1·9	0·10	0·03	4·3	0·9	Tr.		13
330	Plums, cooking, raw ..	0·2	Tr.	1·8	7	0·6	55	3·9	2·2	0·09	0·03	4·1	1·3	Tr.		15
330*a*	Plums, cooking, raw (weighed with stones)	0·2	Tr.	1·6	7	0·5	50	3·6	2·0	0·08	0·02	3·7	1·2	Tr.		13
331	Plums, stewed without sugar (weighed with stones)	0·1	Tr.	1·1	5	0·4	36	2·5	1·4	0·05	0·02	2·7	0·9	Tr.		10
332	Pomegranate juice ..	0·1	Tr.	3·3	13	0·3	58	0·8	0·9	0·04	0·02	2·1	1·2	14·9		10
333	Prunes, dried, raw ..	0·7	Tr.	11·4	46	3·5	246	10·7	7·6	0·82	0·05	23·5	5·3	0·7		58
333*a*	Prunes, dried, raw (weighed with stones)	0·6	Tr.	9·5	38	2·9	204	8·9	6·3	0·68	0·04	19·6	4·4	0·6		48
334	Prunes, stewed without sugar (weighed with stones)	0·3	Tr.	4·4	18	1·3	95	4·1	2·9	0·32	0·02	9·1	2·0	0·3		22
335	Quinces	0·1	Tr.	1·8	7	0·9	58	4·0	1·7	0·09	0·04	5·4	1·5	0·5		14
336	Raisins, dried	0·3	Tr.	18·3	70	14·9	244	17·2	11·8	0·44	0·07	9·3	6·5	2·4		76
337	Raspberries, raw ..	0·3	Tr.	1·6	7	0·7	64	11·6	6·2	0·34	0·06	8·2	4·9	6·3		17
338	Raspberries, stewed without sugar	0·2	Tr.	1·1	5	0·5	43	7·9	4·2	0·23	0·04	5·5	3·3	4·3		12
339	Rhubarb, raw	0·2	Tr.	0·3	2	0·6	121	29·2	3·9	0·11	0·04	6·0	2·3	24·7		37
340	Rhubarb, stewed without sugar	0·1	Tr.	0·2	1	0·4	85	20·4	2·7	0·08	0·04	4·2	1·6	17·3		26
341	Strawberries	0·2	Tr.	1·8	7	0·4	46	6·3	3·3	0·20	0·04	6·5	3·8	5·0		10
342	Sultanas, dried ..	0·5	Tr.	18·4	71	15·0	243	14·9	10·0	0·52	0·10	26·8	12·6	4·4		58
343	Tangerines	0·3	Tr.	2·3	10	0·6	44	11·8	3·2	0·08	0·03	4·7	2·9	0·7		15
343*a*	Tangerines (weighed with peel and pips)	0·2	Tr.	1·6	7	0·4	31	8·3	2·2	0·05	0·02	3·3	2·0	0·5		11

Nuts

No.	Food.	g. per oz. Protein (N × 6·25).	Fat.	Available carbohydrate (as monosaccharides).	Calories per oz.	mg. per oz. Na.	K.	Ca.	Mg.	Fe.	Cu.	P.	S.	Cl.	Acid-base balance, c.c. per oz. $\frac{N}{10}$ Acid.	$\frac{N}{10}$ Alkali.
344	Almonds	5·8	15·2	1·2	170	1·6	243	70·0	73·0	1·20	0·04	126	41	0·5		52
344*a*	Almonds (weighed with shells)	2·2	5·6	0·5	63	0·6	90	26·0	27·0	0·44	0·01	47	15	0·2		19
345	Barcelona nuts ..	3·7	18·2	1·5	189	0·7	266	48·2	57·2	0·84	0·27	85	50	9·5		52
345*a*	Barcelona nuts (weighed with shells)	2·3	11·3	0·9	117	0·4	165	30·0	35·5	0·52	0·17	53	31	5·9		32
346	Brazil nuts	3·9	17·3	1·2	183	0·4	216	50·0	117·0	0·80	0·31	168	83	17·3		13
346*a*	Brazil nuts (weighed with shells)	1·8	7·8	0·5	82	0·2	97	22·4	52·6	0·36	0·14	76	37	7·8		6
347	Chestnuts	0·7	0·8	10·4	49	3·1	141	13·1	9·4	0·25	0·07	21	8	4·3		32
347*a*	Chestnuts (weighed with shells)	0·5	0·6	8·6	40	2·6	117	10·8	7·8	0·21	0·05	17	7	3·5		27
348	Cob nuts	2·6	10·2	1·9	113	0·4	98	12·5	15·9	0·30	0·06	65	21	1·7	11	
348*a*	Cob nuts (weighed with shells)	0·9	3·7	0·7	41	0·1	35	4·5	5·7	0·11	0·02	23	8	0·6	4	
349	Coconut, fresh	1·1	10·2	1·1	104	4·7	124	3·7	14·8	0·59	0·09	27	13	32·4		14
350	Coconut milk	0·1	—	1·4	—	29·8	89	8·2	8·5	0·03	0·01	11	7	52·0		21
351	Coconut, desiccated ..	1·9	17·6	1·8	178	8·1	214	6·4	25·5	1·02	0·16	46	22	55·8		24
352	Peanuts	8·0	13·9	2·4	171	1·6	193	17·3	51·3	0·58	0·08	104	107	1·9	33	
352*a*	Peanuts (weighed with shells)	5·5	9·6	1·7	118	1·1	133	11·9	35·5	0·40	0·05	72	74	1·3	23	
353	Walnuts	3·6	14·6	1·4	156	0·8	195	17·3	37·2	0·67	0·09	145	30	6·5	24	
353*a*	Walnuts (weighed with shells)	2·3	9·4	0·9	100	0·5	124	11·1	23·8	0·43	0·06	93	19	4·2	15	

Vegetables

No.	Food.	g. per oz. Protein (N × 6·25).	Fat.	Available carbohydrate (as monosaccharides).	Calories per oz.	mg. per oz. Na.	K.	Ca.	Mg.	Fe.	Cu.	P.	S.	Cl.	Acid-base balance, c.c. per oz. N/10 Acid.	N/10 Alkali.
354	Artichokes, globe, boiled	0·3	Tr.	*0·8	4	4·2	93	12·4	7·7	0·14	0·03	11·3	4·4	23·7		22
354a	Artichokes, globe, boiled (weighed as served)	0·1	Tr.	*0·3	2	1·8	40	5·3	3·3	0·06	0·01	4·9	1·9	10·2		9
355	Artichokes, Jerusalem, boiled	0·5	Tr.	*0·9	5	0·7	119	8·6	3·2	0·12	0·03	9·4	6·1	16·4		23
356	Asparagus, boiled ..	1·0	Tr.	0·3	5	0·5	67	7·3	3·0	0·25	0·06	24·0	13·2	8·9	3	
356a	Asparagus, boiled (weighed as served)	0·5	Tr.	0·2	3	0·3	34	3·7	1·5	0·13	0·03	12·0	6·6	4·5	1	
357	Beans, baked	1·7	0·1	4·9	26	(168)	98	17·4	10·4	0·58	0·07	52·1	14·4	(230)		8
358	Beans, broad, boiled ..	1·2	Tr.	2·0	12	5·6	66	6·0	7·8	0·28	0·12	28·1	7·7	4·0		5
359	Beans, butter, raw ..	5·5	Tr.	14·2	76	17·4	485	24·1	46·5	1·68	0·35	90·4	31·1	13·2		101
360	Beans, butter, boiled ..	2·0	Tr.	4·9	26	4·6	113	5·3	9·5	0·47	0·05	24·5	13·4	0·7		17
361	Beans, French, boiled ..	0·2	Tr.	0·3	2	1·0	29	11·0	2·9	0·17	0·03	4·3	2·4	3·0		11
362	Beans, haricot, raw ..	6·1	Tr.	12·9	73	12·3	329	51·1	52·0	1·89	0·17	87·8	47·3	0·5		72
363	Beans, haricot, boiled ..	1·9	Tr.	4·7	25	4·3	91	18·3	12·6	0·71	0·04	34·6	13·1	0·3		14
364	Beans, runner, raw ..	0·3	Tr.	0·8	4	1·8	78	9·5	6·5	0·21	0·03	7·4	4·0	6·5		22
365	Beans, runner, boiled ..	0·2	Tr.	0·3	2	0·9	25	7·3	3·6	0·17	0·01	3·0	2·7	2·5		9
366	Beetroot, boiled.. ..	0·5	Tr.	2·8	13	18·2	99	8·5	4·8	0·20	0·04	10·1	6·3	21·5		25
367	Broccoli tops, boiled ..	0·9	Tr.	0·1	4	1·9	29	45·4	3·8	0·43	0·03	15·3	12·8	14·5		12
368	Brussels sprouts, boiled	0·7	Tr.	0·5	5	2·2	70	7·7	3·0	0·18	0·02	12·7	22·0	3·2		2
369	Cabbage, red, raw ..	0·5	Tr.	1·0	6	9·0	86	15·1	4·7	0·16	0·03	9·1	19·3	12·6		16
370	Cabbage, Savoy, raw ..	0·9	Tr.	0·9	7	6·4	75	21·3	5·5	0·26	—	19·2	25·0	6·3		7
371	Cabbage, Savoy, boiled..	0·4	Tr.	0·3	3	2·3	35	14·9	2·0	0·20	0·02	7·7	8·6	2·7		8
372	Cabbage, spring, boiled	0·3	Tr.	0·2	2	3·5	31	8·5	1·8	0·13	0·02	9·0	7·6	1·8		4
373	Cabbage, winter, raw ..	0·8	Tr.	2·4	12	8·1	68	20·6	4·8	0·35	—	18·2	20·3	11·2		8
374	Cabbage, winter, boiled	0·2	Tr.	0·4	3	3·8	41	16·6	2·1	0·13	0·01	4·6	6·7	3·9		14

* This vegetable contains inulin. 50 per cent. total carbohydrate taken to be available.

Vegetables—*continued*

No.	Food.	Protein (N × 6·25). g. per oz.	Fat. g. per oz.	Available carbohydrate (as monosaccharides). g. per oz.	Calories per oz.	Na. mg. per oz.	K.	Ca.	Mg.	Fe.	Cu.	P.	S.	Cl.	N/10 Acid. Acid-base balance, c.c. per oz.	N/10 Alkali.
375	Carrageen moss, dried ..	1·9	Tr.	0·1	8	823·0	596	240·0	179·0	2·52	0·15	58·3	1550·0	327·0	320	
376	Carrots, old, raw ..	0·2	Tr.	1·5	6	27·0	64	13·6	3·4	0·16	0·02	6·0	2·0	19·5		26
377	Carrots, old, boiled ..	0·2	Tr.	1·2	5	14·2	25	10·4	1·8	0·11	0·02	4·7	1·4	8·8		13
378	Carrots, young, boiled ..	0·3	Tr.	1·3	6	6·4	67	8·2	2·4	0·12	0·02	8·4	2·6	7·8		17
379	Cauliflower, boiled ..	0·4	Tr.	0·3	3	3·2	43	6·5	1·9	0·14	0·02	9·4	8·4	3·3		5
380	Celeriac, boiled	0·5	Tr.	0·6	4	8·0	114	13·2	3·4	0·24	0·04	20·2	3·6	6·6		25
381	Celery, raw	0·3	Tr.	0·4	3	38·9	79	14·8	2·7	0·17	0·03	9·0	4·2	52·0		24
382	Celery, boiled	0·2	Tr.	0·2	1	18·9	38	14·8	2·4	0·12	0·03	5·5	2·4	28·4		14
383	Chicory, raw	0·2	Tr.	*0·4	3	2·1	52	5·2	3·6	0·20	0·04	5·9	3·6	7·1		12
384	Cucumber, raw	0·2	Tr.	0·5	3	3·7	40	6·5	2·6	0·09	0·03	6·9	3·1	6·9		9
385	Egg plant, raw	0·2	Tr.	0·9	4	0·7	68	3·0	2·7	0·11	0·02	3·4	2·6	17·3		13
386	Endive, raw	0·5	Tr.	0·3	3	2·9	108	12·4	3·0	0·79	0·03	18·9	7·3	20·0		15
387	Horseradish, raw ..	1·3	Tr.	3·1	17	2·2	164	33·8	10·2	0·58	0·04	19·9	60·2	5·3		17
388	Leeks, boiled	0·5	Tr.	1·3	7	1·8	79	17·2	3·6	0·57	0·03	7·8	13·9	12·1		15
389	Lentils, raw	6·8	Tr.	15·1	84	10·2	192	11·0	21·7	2·17	0·17	69·0	34·8	18·0		6
390	Lentils, boiled	1·9	Tr.	5·2	27	2·7	62	3·0	5·9	0·63	0·08	22·7	10·6	3·6		1
391	Lettuce, raw	0·3	Tr.	0·5	3	0·9	59	7·4	2·8	0·21	0·04	8·6	3·4	11·2		11
392	Marrow, boiled	0·1	Tr.	0·4	2	0·3	24	3·9	1·9	0·06	0·01	3·6	1·6	3·9		5
393	Mushrooms, raw ..	†0·5	Tr.	0·0	2	2·6	133	0·8	3·8	0·29	0·18	38·6	9·6	24·0		1
394	Mushrooms, fried ..	†0·6	6·4	0·0	62	3·1	161	1·0	4·6	0·36	0·22	47·2	20·9	29·3	5	
395	Mustard and cress, raw ..	0·5	Tr.	0·3	3	5·4	96	18·7	7·8	1·29	0·03	18·6	48·2	25·3	7	
396	Onions, raw	0·3	Tr.	1·5	7	2·9	39	8·9	2·2	0·09	0·02	8·5	14·4	5·5		1
397	Onions, boiled	0·2	Tr.	0·8	4	1·9	22	6·9	1·4	0·07	0·02	4·7	6·7	1·4		1
398	Onions, fried	0·5	9·5	2·9	101	5·7	76	17·4	4·2	0·17	0·05	16·8	24·9	10·8		5
399	Onions, spring, raw ..	0·3	Tr.	2·4	10	3·7	64	38·4	3·1	0·35	0·04	6·7	14·2	10·1		24
400	Parsley, raw	1·5	Tr.	Tr.	6	9·4	307	92·2	14·8	2·27	0·15	36·3	—	44·3	—	—
401	Parsnips, raw	0·5	Tr.	3·2	14	47·0	97	15·6	6·4	0·16	0·03	19·6	4·7	11·5		21
402	Parsnips, boiled	0·4	Tr.	3·8	16	1·2	83	10·1	3·7	0·13	0·03	9·0	4·1	9·3		19

403	Peas, fresh, raw	1·6	Tr.	3·0	18	0·1	97	4·3	8·6	0·53	0·07	29·5	14·2	10·8		3
404	Peas, fresh, boiled ..	1·4	Tr.	2·2	14	Tr.	49	3·6	6·1	0·35	0·04	23·6	12·4	2·2	4	
405	Peas, dried, raw ..	6·1	Tr.	14·2	78	10·8	280	17·2	33·0	1·34	0·14	86·0	36·7	17·0		29
406	Peas, dried, boiled ..	2·0	Tr.	5·4	28	3·6	76	6·9	8·6	0·41	0·05	32·1	11·1	2·6		3
407	Peas, split, dried, raw ..	6·3	Tr.	16·1	86	10·9	258	9·4	35·5	1·54	0·16	76·1	47·1	15·9		22
408	Peas, split, dried, boiled	2·3	Tr.	6·2	33	4·0	76	3·1	8·6	0·49	0·07	34·6	13·0	2·9	1	
409	Peas, tinned	1·7	Tr.	4·7	24	(74)	57	7·3	6·9	0·53	0·06	48·0	12·4	(90)	8	
410	Potatoes, old, raw ..	0·6	Tr.	5·9	25	1·9	161	2·2	6·9	0·21	0·04	11·4	9·8	22·3		29
411	Potatoes, old, raw, peel	0·7	Tr.	4·5	20	2·0	184	7·7	7·8	0·57	0·07	10·3	—	26·9	—	—
412	Potatoes, old, boiled ..	0·4	Tr.	5·6	23	1·0	92	1·2	4·3	0·14	0·03	8·2	6·3	11·6		16
413	Potatoes, old, mashed ..	0·4	1·4	5·1	34	(7)	86	3·3	4·1	0·13	0·03	9·3	6·4	(20)		14
414	Potatoes, old, baked in skins	0·7	Tr.	7·1	30	2·2	193	2·6	8·3	0·25	0·05	13·7	11·8	26·8		35
414*a*	Potatoes, old, baked in skins (weighed with skins)	0·6	Tr.	5·8	24	1·8	156	2·1	6·7	0·20	0·04	11·1	9·5	21·7		28
415	Potatoes, old, roast ..	0·8	0·3	7·8	35	2·4	211	2·9	9·1	0·28	0·06	15·1	16·0	29·3		36
416	Potatoes, old, " chips " ..	1·1	2·6	10·6	68	3·3	290	3·9	12·3	0·38	0·08	20·6	12·7	39·8		56
417	Potatoes, new, boiled ..	0·5	Tr.	5·2	21	11·5	94	1·4	5·6	0·13	0·04	9·4	6·9	12·9		20
418	Pumpkin, raw	0·2	Tr.	1·0	4	0·4	88	11·1	2·3	0·11	0·02	5·5	2·7	10·4		22
419	Radishes, raw	0·3	Tr.	0·8	4	16·8	68	12·4	3·2	0·54	0·04	7·7	10·6	5·3		20
420	Salsify, boiled	0·5	Tr.	*0·8	5	2·4	52	17·0	4·0	0·35	0·03	15·0	7·2	13·0		8
421	Seakale, boiled	0·4	Tr.	0·2	2	1·1	14	13·6	3·0	0·17	0·02	9·5	14·8	3·5	3	
422	Spinach, boiled	1·4	Tr.	0·4	7	34·9	139	169·0	16·8	1·14	0·07	26·4	24·6	15·8		112
423	Spring greens, boiled ..	0·5	Tr.	0·3	3	2·9	34	24·4	2·4	0·38	0·02	8·7	8·1	4·6		12
424	Swedes, raw	0·3	Tr.	1·2	6	14·8	39	16·0	3·1	0·10	0·01	5·4	11·1	8·7		14
425	Swedes, boiled	0·3	Tr.	1·1	5	4·1	29	11·8	2·0	0·08	0·01	5·2	8·7	2·6		8
426	Sweet potatoes, boiled ..	0·3	Tr.	5·7	23	5·1	84	5·8	3·5	0·18	0·04	12·4	4·2	17·0		14
427	Tomatoes, raw	0·3	Tr.	0·8	4	0·8	82	3·8	3·1	0·12	0·03	6·1	3·0	14·5		16
428	Tomatoes, fried	0·3	1·7	0·9	20	0·9	95	4·4	3·6	0·14	0·03	7·1	2·6	16·8		19
429	Turnips, raw	0·2	Tr.	1·1	5	16·5	68	16·7	2·1	0·11	0·02	7·8	6·3	19·9		18
430	Turnips, boiled	0·2	Tr.	0·7	3	8·0	45	15·6	1·9	0·10	0·01	5·4	6·0	8·9		15
431	Turnip tops, boiled ..	0·8	Tr.	Tr.	3	1·9	22	27·8	2·9	0·88	0·03	12·8	11·1	4·2		6
432	Watercress, raw ..	0·8	Tr.	0·2	4	17·0	89	63·0	4·8	0·46	0·04	14·8	36·1	44·4		21

* This vegetable contains inulin. 50 per cent. total carbohydrate taken to be available. † *See* p. 6.

Sugar, Preserves and Sweetmeats

No.	Food.	g. per oz.			Calories per oz.	mg. per oz.									Acid-base balance, c.c. per oz.	
		Protein (N.× 6·25).	Fat.	Available carbohydrate (as monosaccharides).		Na.	K.	Ca.	Mg.	Fe.	Cu.	P.	S.	Cl.	$\frac{N}{10}$ Acid.	$\frac{N}{10}$ Alkali.
433	Blackcurrant purée ..	0·1	Tr.	11·4	43	3·1	57	9·7	3·4	0·45	0·04	7·1	9·1	3·7		12
434	Cherries, glacé	0·2	0·0	15·8	60	18·4	5	12·6	2·3	0·82	0·36	4·1	6·0	20·2		5
435	Chocolate, blended (1943)	2·6	10·2	14·9	161	(78)	110	72·0	18·8	0·58	0·14	64·0	—	52·0	—	—
436	Chocolate, milk (1935) ..	2·1	9·7	14·9	154	26·5	138	49·8	16·3	0·47	0·04	61·0	19·0	37·7		24
437	Chocolate, milk (1943) ..	2·5	10·7	15·5	167	(78)	99	69·9	16·7	0·49	0·14	62·0	—	48·2	—	—
438	Chocolate, plain (1935) ..	1·3	9·2	16·6	153	5·3	113	7·4	23·2	0·93	0·32	39·5	9·1	2·5		22
439	Chocolate, plain (1943) ..	1·6	10·0	14·9	155	(41)	73	17·9	37·2	0·82	0·23	39·2	—	1·4	—	—
440	Chutney, apple	0·2	Tr.	14·8	57	(48)	62	7·8	5·1	0·29	0·03	9·6	9·1	(71)		13
441	Chutney, tomato ..	0·3	Tr.	11·0	43	(37)	79	7·4	5·1	0·26	0·03	10·4	8·8	(61)		15
442	Comb honey	0·2	*1·3	21·2	80	2·0	10	2·2	0·6	0·06	0·01	9·2	0·2	7·5	3	
443	Honey, in jars	0·1	Tr.	21·7	82	3·1	15	1·5	0·6	0·11	0·01	4·8	0·2	5·1		2
444	Ice cream	1·1	3·8	5·0	58	18·2	51	43·4	4·3	0·06	0·01	27·1	8·7	29·2		15
445	Jam, fruit with edible seeds	0·2	0·0	19·6	74	4·5	32	6·9	2·9	0·42	0·07	5·1	1·8	2·6		11
446	Jam, stone fruit ..	0·1	0·0	19·7	74	3·5	30	3·4	1·5	0·29	0·03	5·2	0·9	1·0		8
447	Jelly, packet	†1·7	0·0	17·7	73	7·2	7	8·9	1·3	0·49	0·05	2·0	10·4	8·5		<1
448	Lemon curd	0·9	3·9	12·0	86	(18)	19	5·2	1·4	0·20	0·01	17·8	13·4	(24)	10	
449	Marmalade	Tr.	0·0	19·8	74	5·2	12	9·9	1·1	0·16	0·03	3·6	0·6	2·0		8
450	Mincemeat	0·2	0·9	7·2	37	(59)	159	14·9	5·9	0·60	0·02	4·5	8·1	(129)		35
451	Sugar, Demerara ..	0·1	0·0	‡29·6	112	1·8	25	4·9	4·2	0·25	0·02	5·7	4·0	10·0		9
452	Sugar, white	Tr.	0·0	‡29·7	112	0·1	1	0·4	0·1	0·01	0·01	Tr.	Tr.	Tr.		<1
453	Syrup, golden	0·1	0·0	22·4	84	76·6	69	7·5	2·7	0·41	0·03	5·7	15·3	11·8		41
454	Toffee, home made ..	0·1	1·8	25·6	113	(33)	26	3·1	1·1	0·16	0·01	2·8	5·9	(11)		15
455	Treacle, black	0·3	0·0	19·1	73	27·2	416	140·5	40·9	2·60	0·12	8·7	19·5	231·0		140

* *See* note p. 93. † *See* p. 6. ‡ *See* p. 6.

Beverages

No.	Food.	g. per oz.			Calories per oz.	mg. per oz.									Acid-base balance, c.c. per oz.	
		Protein.	Fat.	Available carbohydrate (as monosaccharides).		Na.	K.	Ca.	Mg.	Fe.	Cu.	P.	S.	Cl.	$\frac{N}{10}$ Acid.	$\frac{N}{10}$ Alkali.
456	Bournvita	3·2	2·1	19·2	105	102·0	188	25·3	48·2	0·94	0·28	116·7	69·0	52·5		13
457	Bovril	*8·3	0·2	0·0	36	(1580)	1020	14·8	48·0	3·44	0·24	369·0	103·0	(1950)		145
458	Cocoa powder	5·8	6·6	9·9	128	(185)	152	14·6	54·5	4·06	0·97	194·0	45·5	56·5		2
459	Coffee, ground, roasted ..	3·6	4·4	8·1	85	20·8	575	37·8	66·8	1·16	0·23	45·7	31·3	6·7		180
460	Coffee, infusion, 2 min. ..	0·1	Tr.	0·1	1	Tr.	19	0·6	1·6	Tr.	Tr.	0·4	—	Tr.	—	—
461	Coffee, infusion, 5 min. ..	0·1	Tr.	0·1	1	Tr.	25	1·0	2·4	Tr.	Tr.	0·8	—	Tr.	—	—
462	Coffee, infusion, 10 min.	0·1	Tr.	0·1	1	Tr.	30	1·1	3·0	Tr.	Tr.	1·2	—	Tr.	—	—
463	Coffee, infusion, 20 min.	0·1	Tr.	0·1	1	Tr.	31	1·1	3·1	Tr.	Tr.	1·4	—	Tr.	—	—
464	Lemonade	Tr.	Tr.	3·5	13	Tr.	4	0·2	0·2	Tr.	Tr.	0·3	Tr.	Tr.		1
465	Malted milk, Horlick's ..	4·1	2·4	20·1	114	196·0	321	77·2	20·0	0·37	0·35	114·0	47·5	146·0		78
466	Marmite	*2·8	Tr.	0·0	12	(1740)	978	22·0	78·4	1·48	0·56	535·0	108·0	(2200)		49
467	Ovaltine	3·7	2·2	17·4	101	70·8	312	96·1	39·8	0·99	0·18	160·0	52·0	115·0		24
468	Oxo cubes	*9·0	1·1	0·0	47	(3010)	761	28·8	45·4	3·98	0·09	310·0	91·0	(3980)		180
469	Tea, Indian	4·4	0·0	0·0	17	12·6	612	121·0	72·0	4·32	0·45	178·0	50·2	14·7		132
470	Tea, Indian, infusion ..	Tr.	0·0	0·0	<1	Tr.	5	0·1	0·3	Tr.	Tr.	0·3	—	Tr.	—	—
471	Virol	1·3	3·6	16·9	102	(106)	102	30·6	17·4	5·00	0·13	75·5	23·5	(169)	9	

*See pp. 6 and 95.

Beers (1938)

No.	Food.	c.c. per pint Alcohol	g. per pint. Protein (N × 6·25).	Fat.	Available carbohydrate (as monosaccharides).	Calories per pint.	mg. per pint. Na.	K.	Ca.	Mg.	Fe.	Cu.	P.	S.	Cl.	Acid-base balance, c.c. per pint. $\frac{N}{10}$ Acid.	$\frac{N}{10}$ Alkali.
472	Mild ale, draught	25·2	2·8	Tr.	17·4	252	130	235	66	43·1	0·28	0·73	83	114	203		3
473	Mild ale, bottled	26·8	1·7	Tr.	20·7	273	109	303	71	56·0	0·45	0·39	101	141	202	4	
474	Pale ale, draught	33·7	1·7	Tr.	17·9	310	76	314	61	58·9	0·28	0·45	120	130	198	21	
475	Pale ale, bottled	34·5	1·1	Tr.	16·8	308	76	291	76	58·9	0·39	0·34	99	134	177	2	
476	Strong ale ..	45·0	2·8	Tr.	27·4	428	108	499	95	80·7	0·56	0·62	160	191	305	19	
477	Stout	26·7	2·2	Tr.	23·0	282	117	381	58	65·0	0·78	0·67	130	130	200		10

Condiments

No.	Food.	g. per oz. Protein (N × 6·25).	Fat.	Available carbohydrate (as monosaccharides).	Calories per oz.	mg. per oz. Na.	K.	Ca.	Mg.	Fe.	Cu.	P.	S.	Cl.	Acid-base balance, c.c. per oz. $\frac{N}{10}$ Acid.	$\frac{N}{10}$ Alkali.
478	Curry powder	2·7	3·1	7·4	67	128	520	181	81	21·30	0·30	77	24	134		244
479	Ground ginger	2·1	*0·9	17·0	74	10	258	28	38	4·90	0·13	39	41	11		61
480	Mustard	8·2	8·1	5·9	132	1	268	95	73	3·10	0·06	50	364	18	88	
481	Pepper	2·5	*1·8	19·3	88	2	12	36	13	2·90	0·32	37	28	17		82
482	Salt, block	0·0	0·0	0·0	0	11,000	Tr.	65	10	0·07	0·11	Tr.	114	16,900	30	
483	Table salt "A"† ..	0·0	0·0	0·0	0	11,000	Tr.	42	142	0·15	0·16	21	10	17,000		120
484	Table salt "B"† ..	0·0	0·0	0·0	0	11,200	Tr.	3	50	0·09	0·19	Tr.	7	17,200		40
485	Vinegar	0·1	0·0	0·2	1	6	25	4	6	0·13	0·01	9	5	13		3

* *See* note p. 97. † *See* note p. 96.

Vegetable Fats

No.	Food.	g. per oz. Protein (N × 6·25).	Fat.	Carbohydrate.	Calories per oz.	mg. per oz. Na.	K.	Ca.	Mg.	Fe.	Cu.	P.	S.	Cl.	Acid-base balance. c.c. per oz. $\frac{N}{10}$ Acid.	$\frac{N}{10}$ Alkali.
486	Margarine	0·1	24·2	0·0	226	(90)	1	1·2	0·3	0·09	0·01	3·4	3·4	(141)	4	
487	Olive oil	Tr.	28·4	0·0	264	Tr.	Tr.	0·1	0·1	0·02	0·02	Tr.	Tr.	Tr.		<1

Cakes and Pastries

No.	Food.	g. per oz. Protein.	Fat.	Available carbohydrate (as monosaccharides).	Calories per oz.	mg. per oz. Na.	K.	Ca.	Mg.	Fe.	Cu.	P.	S.	Cl.	Acid-base balance, c.c. per oz. $\frac{N}{10}$ Acid.	$\frac{N}{10}$ Alkali.
488	Buns (1943)	2·5	1·7	16·2	87	(34)	56	(23)	13·1	0·77	0·09	48·3	—	(37)	—	—
489	Cherry cake	1·3	6·8	16·0	129	(39)	20	9·1	2·9	0·35	0·09	20·1	17·9	(36)	5	
490	Chocolate cakes	1·8	6·6	15·8	128	(61)	26	6·4	4·0	0·36	0·02	29·2	23·8	(51)	8	
491	Coconut cakes	2·0	6·6	15·5	128	(47)	49	9·9	6·5	0·31	0·03	28·8	23·5	(48)	3	
492	Currant buns (1936) ..	2·1	2·2	15·4	87	(29)	52	10·2	6·3	0·60	0·02	18·4	20·8	(55)	5	
493	Currant cake	1·7	5·2	17·2	120	(43)	59	9·8	5·0	0·33	0·04	24·1	21·8	(42)		9
494	Currant cake (1943) ..	1·9	3·1	14·6	91	(169)	60	(19)	9·7	0·69	0·08	(93)	—	(96)	—	—
495	Doughnuts	1·7	4·5	13·8	101	(17)	32	6·1	4·7	0·46	0·03	15·6	16·0	(25)	5	
496	Dundee cake	1·1	4·3	17·7	110	(40)	96	14·3	7·8	0·57	0·05	22·3	15·6	(51)		17
497	Eccles cakes	1·4	8·3	14·6	138	(47)	51	7·1	4·7	0·23	0·04	16·2	16·2	(78)	2	
498	Ginger biscuits	1·7	4·7	20·2	127	(94)	40	6·1	4·3	0·36	0·02	21·6	23·1	(40)		18
499	Gingerbread	1·6	3·7	18·0	109	(95)	45	10·1	4·4	0·36	0·02	23·0	22·2	(30)		25
500	Ginger cake (1943) ..	1·9	2·6	15·5	90	(276)	43	(19)	10·9	1·33	0·07	(133)	—	(93)	—	—
501	Jam tarts, flaky pastry	0·7	4·5	16·0	105	(29)	27	4·3	2·9	0·27	0·03	10·3	8·8	(45)	1	
502	Jam tarts, short pastry	0·9	3·8	17·3	104	(33)	29	4·5	3·2	0·28	0·03	11·9	10·5	(51)	2	
503	Jam tarts, economical ..	1·7	5·6	18·3	128	(47)	35	(36)	7·9	0·47	0·09	(67)	—	(45)	—	—
504	Lemon curd tarts ..	1·6	6·9	14·3	125	(50)	25	4·6	3·5	0·21	0·01	20·0	19·0	(78)	14	
505	Mince pies	1·3	5·6	12·2	103	(43)	76	7·9	5·1	0·35	0·02	14·3	16·5	(116)		3

Cakes and Pastries—*continued*

No.	Food.	g. per oz.			Calories per oz.	mg. per oz.									Acid-base balance, c.c. per oz.	
		Protein.	Fat.	Available carbohydrate (as monosaccharides).		Na.	K.	Ca.	Mg.	Fe.	Cu.	P.	S.	Cl.	$\frac{N}{10}$ Acid.	$\frac{N}{10}$ Alkali.
506	Oatmeal biscuits ..	2·5	6·8	17·7	143	(78)	57	10·2	15·0	0·61	0·04	57·8	31·8	(38)	2	
507	Oatmeal biscuits, economical	2·7	5·3	20·8	139	(34)	70	(20)	20·6	0·82	0·08	71·3	—	(61)	—	—
508	Orange cake	1·7	7·2	15·3	132	(56)	26	5·9	3·3	0·28	0·01	24·9	22·3	(54)	8	
509	Pastry, flaky, raw ..	1·3	8·4	10·2	121	(49)	19	2·7	3·1	0·15	0·01	14·1	15·0	(82)	11	
510	Pastry, flaky, baked ..	1·5	10·2	12·4	147	(62)	23	3·3	3·8	0·18	0·01	17·0	18·2	(100)	13	
511	Pastry, short, raw ..	1·6	7·1	12·7	119	(57)	23	3·3	3·9	0·17	0·01	17·0	18·2	(92)	13	
512	Pastry, short, baked ..	1·9	8·6	15·5	146	(70)	28	4·0	4·7	0·21	0·02	20·9	22·3	(113)	15	
513	Pastry, economical, raw	2·0	6·9	14·1	126	(56)	30	(43)	9·1	0·45	0·07	(81)	—	(55)	—	—
514	Pastry, economical, baked	2·4	8·3	17·0	152	(68)	36	(52)	10·9	0·55	0·08	(98)	—	(67)	—	—
515	Pastry, potato, raw ..	2·0	4·2	13·9	99	(109)	52	(13)	9·4	0·43	0·06	29·8	—	(175)	—	—
516	Pastry, potato, baked ..	2·6	5·4	18·1	129	(142)	68	(16)	12·2	0·57	0·09	39·0	—	(228)	—	—
517	Plain biscuits, economical	2·7	6·0	20·1	142	(43)	37	(36)	9·5	0·58	0·07	(76)	—	(46)	—	—
518	Plain cake, economical ..	2·0	5·7	15·0	117	(44)	31	(34)	6·7	0·42	0·06	(67)	—	(46)	—	—
519	Queen cakes	1·7	6·4	16·8	129	(46)	49	9·2	4·4	0·30	0·03	26·8	22·6	(37)	1	
520	Rock buns	1·6	4·8	18·4	120	(44)	54	13·9	5·3	0·21	0·03	22·2	18·1	(41)		7
521	Rock cakes	1·7	4·5	18·6	119	(43)	68	12·0	5·7	0·31	0·05	23·9	21·0	(38)		8
522	Rock cakes, economical	2·2	3·6	18·4	112	(41)	79	(44)	9·7	0·53	0·08	(81)	—	(34)	—	—
523	Scones (with egg) ..	2·4	3·0	17·0	102	(48)	42	13·4	5·7	0·28	0·02	33·4	28·7	(36)	7	
524	Scones (without egg) ..	2·2	3·8	16·3	106	(47)	46	17·9	6·1	0·19	0·02	31·0	24·2	(35)		1
525	Shortbread	1·7	7·7	18·4	148	(24)	26	4·5	4·3	0·18	0·02	19·6	19·5	(40)	13	
526	Sponge cake	2·5	2·0	15·6	88	23	33	9·9	3·9	0·46	0·01	41·2	34·9	29	30	
527	Swiss roll (1943) ..	1·5	0·7	16·3	74	(186)	37	(20)	6·6	0·72	0·16	(100)	—	(69)	—	—
528	Welsh cheese cakes ..	1·3	5·4	17·1	120	(39)	28	5·0	3·5	0·28	0·03	17·5	16·1	(40)	3	

Puddings

No.	Food.	g. per oz. Protein	Fat.	Available carbohydrate (as monosaccharides).	Calories per oz.	mg. per oz. Na.	K.	Ca.	Mg.	Fe.	Cu.	P.	S.	Cl.	Acid-base balance, c.c. per oz. $\frac{N}{10}$ Acid.	$\frac{N}{10}$ Alkali.
529	Apple Charlotte	0·4	4·5	8·1	74	(21)	28	2·1	1·6	0·12	0·03	6·4	3·6	(31)		4
530	Apple dumpling	0·6	2·7	8·1	58	(12)	31	1·9	1·9	0·12	0·03	9·3	7·3	(20)	1	
531	Apple pudding	0·7	3·6	9·1	71	(14)	21	1·8	2·0	0·10	0·02	8·8	8·6	6		1
532	Apple tart	0·6	2·5	9·4	61	(20)	26	1·7	1·8	0·10	0·02	8·3	6·8	(33)	1	
533	Banana custard ..	0·7	0·7	5·2	29	9	64	23·9	6·7	0·07	0·02	21·3	6·9	26		12
534	Blancmange	0·9	1·1	5·3	34	13	44	33·1	3·8	0·05	0·01	26·8	8·0	28		7
535	Bread pudding, economical	1·8	3·2	11·4	80	(60)	57	(17)	7·1	0·45	0·05	(38)	—	(66)	—	—
536	Bread and butter pudding	1·6	2·3	4·9	46	(32)	56	33·7	4·9	0·18	0·02	35·4	16·4	(54)		1
537	Cabinet pudding ..	1·3	1·3	5·8	39	(30)	56	24·7	4·6	0·18	0·02	27·9	9·9	(44)		7
538	Canary pudding	1·8	7·0	15·7	134	(49)	26	7·5	3·6	0·27	0·01	26·6	22·9	(40)	8	
539	Castle pudding, baked ..	1·7	6·8	15·2	130	(47)	24	6·3	3·3	0·26	0·01	25·0	22·1	(38)	8	
540	Castle pudding, steamed	1·5	5·9	13·2	110	(41)	21	5·5	2·9	0·22	0·01	21·8	19·3	(33)	7	
541	Chocolate mould ..	0·9	1·1	6·2	37	16	45	31·9	4·5	0·10	0·02	28·0	8·2	28		7
542	College pudding ..	1·2	6·8	13·8	120	(77)	66	9·4	4·3	0·34	0·04	21·1	16·4	(52)		20
543	Custard, egg, baked ..	1·5	1·7	2·8	32	19	50	36·1	4·3	0·14	0·01	37·1	16·6	35	2	
544	Custard, egg, boiled ..	1·3	1·5	3·8	34	17	44	32·1	3·9	0·13	0·01	33·0	14·7	31	2	
545	Custard, powder ..	0·9	1·1	5·0	33	13	46	34·7	4·0	0·04	0·01	27·9	8·4	28		7
546	Custard tart	1·5	4·1	8·0	74	(37)	38	20·7	4·2	0·16	0·01	27·6	17·1	(60)	6	
547	Dumpling	0·9	3·2	6·8	59	(139)	13	1·8	2·1	0·09	0·01	8·9	10·5	(177)		4
548	Gooseberry tart ..	0·7	2·7	9·0	62	(22)	38	5·3	2·5	0·11	0·02	11·2	9·1	(35)		1
549	Gooseberry tart with potato pastry	1·1	1·9	6·8	47	(49)	57	(11)	4·8	0·25	0·05	18·9	—	(80)	—	—
550	Jam omelette	2·7	4·1	7·7	78	(34)	39	13·9	3·3	0·54	0·02	50·0	39·0	(41)	34	
551	Jam roll, baked ..	1·3	5·4	15·7	114	(43)	28	4·1	3·7	0·24	0·03	14·7	14·4	(39)		1
552	Jelly	*0·6	0·0	5·4	22	2	2	2·7	0·4	0·15	0·02	0·7	3·2	3		<1
553	Jelly, milk	*1·0	0·5	5·9	31	9	25	19·7	2·4	0·16	0·02	14·1	7·2	16		4

* See p. 6.

Puddings—*continued*

No.	Food.	*g. per oz.* Protein.	Fat.	Available carbohydrate (as monosaccharides).	Calories per oz.	*mg. per oz.* Na.	K.	Ca.	Mg.	Fe.	Cu.	P.	S.	Cl.	*Acid-base balance, c.c per oz.* $\frac{N}{10}$ Acid.	$\frac{N}{10}$ Alkali.
554	Pancakes	1·4	4·3	10·6	85	(25)	37	20·8	4·0	0·15	0·01	26·4	15·9	(43)	5	
555	Plum tart (weighed with stones)	0·7	2·7	9·3	62	(22)	34	3·0	2·5	0·10	0·02	8·2	7·4	(35)		2
556	Queen of puddings ..	1·5	2·8	6·7	57	(36)	41	24·8	4·1	0·24	0·02	31·9	17·0	(53)	5	
557	Rhubarb tart	0·7	2·7	8·7	60	(22)	69	15·8	3·4	0·12	0·02	9·3	7·9	(47)		14
558	Rice pudding	1·3	2·6	6·1	52	(18)	54	39·0	4·8	0·04	0·01	34·2	12·1	(38)		5
559	Rice pudding, economical	1·4	0·7	5·4	33	(23)	48	42·3	4·1	0·04	0·05	38·4	—	(42)	—	—
560	Sago pudding	0·9	1·1	5·9	35	14	43	32·8	3·9	0·05	0·01	25·9	7·8	27		8
561	Semolina pudding ..	1·2	1·1	5·7	37	14	49	34·0	4·8	0·06	0·01	29·7	10·7	29		5
562	Suet pudding, plain ..	1·1	5·1	10·6	92	(57)	27	12·7	3·5	0·12	0·01	17·0	11·4	(44)		11
563	Suet pudding with raisins	1·0	4·4	11·8	90	(51)	58	13·1	4·7	0·16	0·02	15·7	10·6	(38)		20
564	Suet pudding with sultanas, economical	1·2	2·6	11·0	70	(20)	53	(32)	5·6	0·26	0·05	(50)	—	12	—	—
565	Syrup sponge pudding, economical	1·5	4·2	15·3	101	(47)	36	(26)	5·3	0·38	0·04	(50)	—	(35)	—	—
566	Tapioca pudding ..	0·9	1·1	6·1	36	14	44	32·9	3·9	0·28	0·01	27·0	8·1	27		7
567	Treacle tart	1·0	3·8	17·8	107	(73)	45	5·5	3·3	0·29	0·02	13·1	17·8	(68)		10
568	Trifle	1·1	1·1	8·0	45	(14)	43	28·2	3·9	0·13	0·01	27·2	11·2	(26)		3
569	Yorkshire pudding ..	2·0	2·7	7·7	62	(117)	49	28·7	5·2	0·19	0·02	36·4	21·1	(188)	8	
570	Yorkshire pudding, economical	1·7	3·2	8·0	67	(158)	23	(44)	6·0	0·36	0·06	(84)	—	(201)	—	—

Meat and Fish Dishes

No.	Food.	g. per oz. Protein.	Fat.	Available carbohydrate (as glucose).	Calories per oz.	mg. per oz. Na.	K.	Ca.	Mg.	Fe.	Cu.	P.	S.	Cl.	Acid-base balance, c.c. per oz. $\frac{N}{10}$ Acid.	$\frac{N}{10}$ Alkali.
571	Beef steak pudding ..	2·9	3·7	6·1	69	(223)	47	2·1	4·4	0·53	—	37·3	30·3	(318)	19	
572	Beef stew	3·1	1·7	0·7	31	(204)	66	3·9	4·7	0·71	—	45·3	33·8	(306)	25	
573	Curried meat	2·3	3·2	2·5	48	(84)	72	9·3	5·8	1·39	—	28·7	27·9	(124)	7	
574	Fish cakes	3·5	4·0	2·8	61	(119)	85	5·6	5·2	0·22	0·04	48·1	41·0	(185)	26	
575	Fish cakes, economical ..	3·0	0·5	4·0	32	(100)	97	7·4	6·3	0·26	0·04	43·8	—	(154)	—	—
576	Fish pie	2·5	4·3	1·9	58	(146)	71	14·6	4·6	0·16	0·02	40·7	30·0	(225)	16	
577	Hot pot	2·8	1·3	3·2	36	(164)	132	6·2	7·1	0·66	—	42·2	33·2	(253)	5	
578	Irish stew	1·1	3·1	2·2	41	(101)	63	2·9	3·4	0·26	—	16·2	14·2	(159)		<1
578a	Irish stew (weighed with bones)	1·0	2·9	2·1	39	(93)	58	2·7	3·1	0·24	—	15·0	13·1	(147)		<1
579	Kedgeree	3·4	2·0	2·8	43	(312)	46	6·0	6·8	0·29	—	47·8	44·8	(459)	33	
580	Sausage roll, flaky pastry	2·1	10·2	10·1	141	(115)	32	3·8	3·8	0·37	0·02	22·6	20·3	(173)	13	
581	Sausage roll, short pastry	2·3	8·8	11·4	134	(128)	36	4·3	4·3	0·41	0·02	25·4	22·6	(189)	13	
582	Sausage roll, short pastry, economical	2·9	7·4	13·3	130	(126)	54	(42)	12·5	0·65	0·09	(87)	—	(154)	—	—
583	Sausage roll, potato pastry	2·8	5·2	13·0	108	(166)	70	(18)	12·5	0·61	0·09	45·2	—	(247)	—	—
584	Shepherd's pie	2·0	1·5	3·5	35	(105)	83	4·3	4·7	0·66	—	25·1	22·8	(166)	4	
585	Steak and kidney pie ..	4·4	5·4	4·8	85	(225)	69	2·9	5·9	1·58	—	60·5	44·4	(339)	40	
586	Toad-in-the-hole ..	2·2	5·8	5·3	83	(199)	46	19·0	4·5	0·40	0·02	35·5	22·8	(297)	9	

Egg and Cheese Dishes

No.	Food.	g. per. oz.			Calories per oz.	mg. per oz.									Acid-base balance, c.c. per oz.	
		Protein.	Fat.	Available carbohydrate (as monosaccharides).		Na.	K.	Ca.	Mg.	Fe.	Cu.	P.	S.	Cl.	$\frac{N}{10}$ Acid.	$\frac{N}{10}$ Alkali.
587	Buck rarebit	4·1	8·7	4·6	114	(122)	35	94·5	8·0	0·31	0·02	80·7	40·7	(195)	16	
588	Cheese omelette ..	5·0	8·8	Tr.	102	(402)	42	89·9	7·3	0·63	0·02	101·0	60·7	(620)	40	
589	Cheese pudding, economical	2·5	2·1	2·9	41	(140)	39	55·3	6·1	0·25	0·04	55·0	—	(217)	—	—
590	Cheese straws	4·7	13·5	7·3	172	(234)	32	116·0	8·9	0·27	0·02	93·0	44·9	(376)	20	
591	Macaroni cheese ..	2·2	3·6	4·3	59	(190)	39	56·6	7·3	0·10	0·01	45·9	19·7	(301)		<1
592	Macaroni cheese, economical	1·6	1·7	3·6	36	(74)	22	41·8	4·7	0·09	0·03	35·5	—	(126)	—	—
593	Omelette	2·2	8·6	0·0	89	(286)	26	11·1	2·4	0·46	0·01	40·7	31·4	(431)	29	
594	Scotch egg	3·1	5·5	2·9	75	(153)	47	10·1	4·0	0·77	0·02	47·2	35·8	(210)	25	
595	Scrambled eggs	2·9	7·1	0·2	79	(358)	38	17·4	3·4	0·59	0·01	54·0	41·0	(540)	36	
596	Scrambled eggs with dried eggs	3·7	7·4	0·0	84	(430)	41	16·3	3·6	0·67	0·02	68·7	53·5	(680)	61	
597	Welsh rarebit	4·3	10·1	5·9	133	(146)	34	116·0	9·3	0·19	0·02	85·7	38·3	(245)	8	

Sauces and Soups

No.	Food.	g. per oz. Protein.	Fat.	Available carbohydrate (as monosaccharides).	Calories per oz.	mg. per oz. Na.	K.	Ca.	Mg.	Fe.	Cu.	P.	S.	Cl.	Acid-base balance, c.c. per oz. $\frac{N}{10}$ Acid.	$\frac{N}{10}$ Alkali
598	Bread sauce	1·1	1·4	3·6	32	(92)	44	29·5	4·4	0·06	0·01	26·1	9·6	(145)		6
599	Bone and vegetable broth	1·1	1·3	0·3	18	(21)	18	4·8	0·9	0·08	0·01	2·8	—	(21)	—	—
600	Bone and vegetable broth (Bickiepegs)	1·3	—	0·1	—	14	12	2·9	1·1	0·08	0·01	2·0	—	16	—	—
601	Cheese sauce	1·9	3·7	2·5	52	(155)	45	57·7	5·4	0·06	0·01	42·6	17·2	(249)		4
602	Egg sauce	1·4	2·9	2·4	41	(133)	45	29·9	4·1	0·14	0·01	32·3	15·6	(209)	1	
603	Onion sauce	0·7	1·6	2·0	25	(86)	36	21·7	3·1	0·06	0·02	17·9	7·9	(137)		6
604	Potato soup	0·6	1·2	3·1	26	(94)	27	13·1	4·5	0·11	0·02	14·8	8·4	(155)	<1	
605	Soup, mixed	0·6	0·4	1·2	10	(62)	38	9·6	2·0	0·40	Tr.	11·4	—	(110)	—	—
606	White sauce, savoury ..	1·1	2·8	2·8	41	(148)	46	32·2	4·2	0·04	0·01	27·3	10·1	(236)		6
607	White sauce, sweet ..	1·0	2·5	5·2	47	18	42	29·5	3·8	0·04	0·01	25·0	9·3	34		5

Vegetable Dishes

No.	Food.	g. per oz. Protein	Fat.	Available carbohydrate (as monosaccharides).	Calories per oz.	mg. per oz. Na.	K.	Ca.	Mg.	Fe.	Cu.	P.	S.	Cl.	Acid-base balance, c.c. per oz. $\frac{N}{10}$ Acid.	$\frac{N}{10}$ Alkali.
608	Potato cakes	1·0	0·1	10·0	43	(177)	104	6·9	7·7	0·28	0·05	17·9	—	(283)	—	—
609	Vegetable pie with potato pastry	0·8	1·0	6·1	36	(121)	99	9·8	6·3	0·23	0·04	14·2	—	(192)	—	—

PHYTIC ACID PHOSPHORUS IN FOODS

	Phytic acid phosphorus as per cent. of total phosphorus.
Cereals and cereal foods—	
All-Bran, Kellogg's	76
Barley, pearl	66
Biscuits, digestive	61
Bread, brown (92%).	55
,, "National wheatmeal" (85%).	30
,, white	15
,, Hovis	38
Cornflakes	25
Flour, English or Manitoba, 100% extraction	70
,, 85% ,,	55
,, 80% ,,	47
,, white	30
Oatmeal, raw	70
Rice, polished	61
Rye, 100% extraction	72
,, 85% ,,	54
,, 75% ,,	44
,, 60% ,,	31
Ryvita	54
Sago	Tr.
Shredded Wheat	80
Soya. Full fat or low fat flour or grits	31
Tapioca	0
Vita-Weat	59
Fruit—	
Apples	0
Bananas	0
Blackberries	16
Figs, dried	13
Prunes, dried	0
Nuts—	
Almonds	82
Barcelona nuts	83
Brazil nuts	86
Chestnuts	18
Cob nuts	74
Coconut	81
Peanuts	57
Walnuts	42
Vegetables—	
Artichokes, Jerusalem, boiled.	25
Beans, broad, boiled	5
,, butter, raw	84
,, haricot, raw	73
Carrots, raw	16
Cauliflower, boiled	0
Celery, raw	0
Lentils, raw	51
Mushrooms, raw	0
Onions, raw	0
Parsnips, raw	31
Peas, fresh, raw	11
,, dried, raw	80
,, split, raw	57
,, tinned	17
Potatoes, old, boiled	19
,, new, boiled	23
Spinach, boiled	0
Swedes, raw	0
Turnips, raw	0
Cocoa and chocolate—	
Chocolate, milk	18
Cocoa	15

ACKNOWLEDGMENTS

For many years A. W. Haynes took an active part in the practical work involved in the preparation of these food tables. We have very much enjoyed his cheerful and efficient co-operation throughout this long period of time, and we take this opportunity of thanking him for all he has done.

ABRAHAMS, M.A., and WIDDOWSON, E. M. (1940) : *Modern Dietary Treatment.* 2nd Ed. Baillière, Tindall and Cox, London.

ASSOCIATION OF OFFICIAL AGRICULTURAL CHEMISTS (1930) : *Official and Tentative Methods of Analysis.* Washington, D.C.

ATWATER, W. O., and BRYANT, A. P. (1906) : The chemical composition of American food materials. *Bull. U.S. Off. Exp. Stas.*, No. 28.

BLACK, D. A. K., and POWELL, J. F. (1942) : Absorption of haemoglobin iron. *Biochem. J.*, **36,** 110.

CHATFIELD, C., and ADAMS, G. (1931) : Proximate composition of fresh vegetables. *Dep. Circ. U.S. Dep. Agric.*, No. 146.

CHATFIELD, C., and MCLAUGHLIN, L. (1928) : Proximate composition of fresh fruits. *Dep. Circ. U.S. Dep. Agric.*, No. 50.

COMMONWEALTH OF AUSTRALIA (1938) : *Fifth Report of the Advisory Council on Nutrition.* Canberra.

IMPERIAL BUREAU OF ANIMAL NUTRITION (1938) : Table of Composition of Foods. *Tech. Comm.*, No. 10.

LEACH, A. E., and WINTON, A. L. (1920) : *Food Inspection and Analysis.* J. Wiley and Son, New York.

MASTERS, M., and MCCANCE, R. A. (1939) : The sulphur content of foods. *Biochem. J.*, **33,** 1304.

MCCANCE, R. A. (1939) : The ionisable and available iron in foods. *Chemistry & Industry*, **58,** 528.

MCCANCE, R. A., EDGECOMBE, C. N., and WIDDOWSON, E. M. (1943) : Phytic acid and iron absorption. *Lancet, Lond.*, **ii,** 126.

MCCANCE, R. A., and LAWRENCE. R. D. (1929) : The carbohydrate content of foods. *Spec. Rep. Ser. Med. Res. Coun., Lond.*, No. 135.

MCCANCE, R. A., SHELDON, W., and WIDDOWSON, E. M. (1934) : Bone and vegetable broth. *Arch. Dis. Child.*, **9,** 251.

MCCANCE, R. A., and SHIPP, H. L. (1933) : The chemistry of flesh foods and their losses on cooking. *Spec. Rep. Ser. Med. Res. Coun., Lond.*, No. 187.

MCCANCE, R. A., and WIDDOWSON, E. M. (1935) : Phytin in human nutrition. *Biochem. J.*, **29**, 2694.

MCCANCE, R. A., and WIDDOWSON, E. M. (1942) : Mineral metabolism of healthy adults on white and brown bread dietaries. *J. Physiol.*, **101,** 44.

MCCANCE, R. A., WIDDOWSON, E. M., and SHACKLETON, L. R. B. (1936) : The nutritive value of fruits, vegetables and nuts. *Spec. Rep. Ser. Med. Res. Coun., Lond.*, No. 213.

MEDICAL RESEARCH COUNCIL (1941) : National flour for bread. M.R.C. Specifications. *Brit. med. J.*, **i,** 828.

MONIER-WILLIAMS, G. W. (1927) : The determination of SO_2 in foods. *Rep. publ. Hlth med. Subj., Lond.*, No. 43.

MOREY, N. B. (1936) : An analysis and comparison of different methods of calculating the energy value of diets. *Nutrit. Abs. Rev.*, **6,** 1.

OLDHAM, H. G. (1941) : The effect of heat on the availability of the iron of beef muscle. *J. Nutrit.*, **22**, 197.

PLIMMER, R. H. A. (1921) : *Analyses and Energy Values of Foods.* H.M. Stationery Office, London.

SCHALL, H. (1939) : *Nahrungsmitteltabelle.* Kurt Kabitzsch, Leipzig.

SHACKLETON, L., and MCCANCE, R. A. (1936) : The ionisable iron in foods. *Biochem. J.*, **30**, 582.

SHERMAN, H. C. (1937) : *Chemistry of Food and Nutrition.* Macmillan, New York.

VON LIEBERMAN, L., and SZEKELY, S. (1898) : Eine neue Methode der Fettbestimmung in Futtermitteln, Fleisch, Koth u.s.w. *Pflüg. Arch. ges. Physiol.*, **72**, 360.

WIDDOWSON, E. M., and MCCANCE, R. A. (1935) : The available carbohydrate of fruits. Determination of glucose, fructose, sucrose and starch. *Biochem. J.*, **29**, 151.

INDEX OF FOODS

LONDON

PRINTED AND PUBLISHED BY HIS MAJESTY'S STATIONERY OFFICE

To be purchased directly from H.M. Stationery Office at the following addresses:
York House, Kingsway, London, W.C.2; 13a Castle Street, Edinburgh, 2;
39 King Street, Manchester, 2; 2 Edmund Street, Birmingham, 3;
1 St. Andrew's Crescent, Cardiff; Tower Lane, Bristol, 1;
80 Chichester Street, Belfast

OR THROUGH ANY BOOKSELLER

1946

(Reprinted 1950)

Price 6*s* 0*d* net

(93302) Wt. 4661 K.6 3/50 (T.S. 20548) S.O. Code No. 45-8-35-45*